JOHN W. MOYER is a taxidermist of wide repute. He has been on the staff of the Chicago Natural History Museum since 1929, and has traveled in nearly every foreign country. Mr. Moyer has contributed articles on taxidermy to the *Encyclopedia Britannica,* the *Britannica Junior,* and the *Encyclopedia Americana,* and is the author of *Trophy Heads,* published by The Ronald Press Company.

EMPEROR PENGUINS, mounted by the author. These birds were collected by the Second Byrd Antarctic Expedition. The habitat group was prepared by the latest known methods in museum taxidermy.

PRACTICAL TAXIDERMY

A Working Guide

By

JOHN W. MOYER

STAFF MEMBER
CHICAGO NATURAL HISTORY MUSEUM

CONTRIBUTOR (TAXIDERMY) TO ENCYCLOPAEDIA
BRITANNICA, ENCYCLOPEDIA AMERICANA

THE RONALD PRESS COMPANY ⏴ NEW YORK

TO MY SON
MICHAEL

PREFACE

The purpose of this book is to describe, in simple language, the latest techniques in the art of taxidermy. The procedures set forth do not involve expensive or elaborate equipment and do not require any previous experience in taxidermy work. Rather, explicit instructions are accompanied by detailed drawings and photographs to guide the amateur in each step of the mounting process. By following these tested and proved methods, the amateur can achieve success in his first effort and increasing expertness with further practice.

The discussion stresses methods which produce mounted specimens that are faithful models of the living animals. The treatment of study-skins for field collections, and the preparation of decorative game heads and fur rugs are fully described. A chapter has been devoted to methods of tanning so that the amateur can complete the entire job of mounting larger animals without incurring the extra expense of professional tanning work. Although the book is intended chiefly for those who have no previous training in taxidermy work, it is believed that the modern museum methods set forth will also be of interest to professional preparators in museums and taxidermy studios.

The author wishes to express his gratitude for the help and encouragement given by Ray Ahrens and Richard Steppan of the former Aard-Vark Studio, Ashley Hine, Leon L. Pray, Julius Friesser, Leon L. Walters, and Dominick Villa, all of the Chicago Natural History (Field) Museum, and Edgar G. Laybourne of the United States National Museum. Credit is due also to Douglas E. Tibbitts and the late Arthur G. Rueckert for their work on the drawings and photographs, and to my wife Helen for her aid in assembling the material used in writing this book.

JOHN W. MOYER

May, 1953

CONTENTS

PRACTICAL TAXIDERMY

Chapter 1

THE EARLY HISTORY OF TAXIDERMY

Taxidermy is the art of preserving the skin, together with the fur, feathers, or scales of animals. The word is derived from the Greek words *taxis*, meaning order, arrangement, or preparation, and *derma*, meaning skin. A skin may be so prepared for use as a specimen for study, as an exhibit in museums and private collections, as an ornament, or article of apparel. Formerly, such mounting of animal skins was called "stuffing" and, in many cases, this was actually what was done (Figure 1). The skin was simply stuffed with straw, excelsior, or other similar material until it looked something like the living animal. Now, however, the stuffing process is entirely obsolete, and great care is taken to model the specimens so they look as lifelike as possible. The old-fashioned "bird-stuffer" has been replaced by the taxidermist, or preparator, and the verb "to stuff," as applied to the art of taxidermy, abandoned. The modern taxidermist mounts, or models a specimen; he does not "stuff" it.

The art of taxidermy as we know it today does not appear to be an ancient one, and is probably not more than 300 years old. This statement, of course, applies only to the mounting of specimens. The curing of skins for use as wearing apparel, rugs, and so forth, was perfected in very early days. Tracing back to the beginnings of taxidermy, one might say that prehistoric man was the first to practice this art by tanning animal skins for use as clothing. The early tribes which inhabited ancient Britain had no other means of covering their bodies and often used the skins of animals as adornments for their persons and in their homes. Our own American Indians preserved the heads of porcupines, foxes, raccoons, loons (Figure 2), and other birds and animals as decorations on clothing and equipment and for use

FIGURE 1

4

in ceremonies. The ancient Egyptians also practiced taxidermy of a sort when they embalmed the bodies of dogs, cats, birds, and other animals, although this embalming was accomplished by the use of spices and oils and not by taxidermy methods. Many mummified remains of these birds and animals have been un-

FIGURE 2

earthed in the tombs of Egypt and are on exhibition in museums throughout the world.

The first attempts at taxidermy date back about 350 years. Specimens of birds were collected in India and skinned, and the skins preserved with spices. These were then brought to Holland where they were arranged and held in a somewhat natural position by wires run through the body and anchored to a perch. The oldest specimen of a mounted animal in existence today is a rhinoceros in the Royal Museum of Vertebrates, Florence, Italy, prepared around the year 1600. The methods used in the mounting of this specimen are not known.

That a crude kind of taxidermy was practiced in England toward the end of the eighteenth century is shown by specimens in the Sloane Collection, which in 1753 formed the nucleus of the British Museum in London. At the great exhibitions held in the middle of the nineteenth century throughout Europe, many examples of British taxidermy were exhibited. In America, the Society of American Taxidermists was founded March 24, 1880, but was disbanded three years later, largely because of a lack of cooperation among the taxidermists of the day. This was the first and only organization of its kind in the United States and lasted only long enough to hold three competitive and general exhibitions; the first in Rochester, the second in Boston, and the third in New York City. These exhibitions gave the public a chance to see the art of taxidermy as it was practiced at that time and brought about much higher standards for exhibits by individuals and museums.

For some time, taxidermy had been carried on throughout the world by a small group of men who were more or less secretive and jealous of their methods with the result that many techniques were not widely known. Later, as the need of museums for highly skilled taxidermists became more and more apparent, information came to be circulated more freely. The publication of books and pamphlets on the subject also contributed to breaking down previous secretiveness.

All the early works published on the subject of taxidermy, such as R. A. F. Réaumur's treatise and the *Guides and Instructions* for collecting and preserving natural history specimens, by E. Donovan and others, are now outmoded and only of historical interest to collectors. For field work and the preparation of specimens for scientific purposes, the instructions contained in the publications of museums are of great assistance. The actual mounting of specimens, however, is so intricate and requires such specialized training that it is rarely undertaken successfully by amateurs. A few works have been published dealing with this branch of taxidermy. The reader who wishes to continue taxidermy as a profession will find much that is helpful in John Rowley's *Taxidermy and Museum Exhibition,* published in 1925.

Rowland Ward's, Ltd., the first important taxidermy studio, was founded about 1850 in London, and is still in existence. The work turned out by this studio helped to improve the methods being used in all branches of taxidermy of that time. Associated with the beginnings of taxidermy in America was the Scudder Museum in New York, the collections of which were later acquired by the famous Peale's Museum of the same city. In 1861, Ward's Natural Science Establishment (in no way connected with Rowland Ward's) was founded by Henry A. Ward at Rochester. This famous institution turned out many of the well-known taxidermists and preparators of the time and was a center for the development of the newer methods practiced today. It was at Ward's that the old "stuffing" methods of mounting animals gave way to the modeling and casting techniques considered later in this book. With such leadership, the art of taxidermy has been developed in America to a higher degree than in any other country of the world.

Chapter 2

FIELD COLLECTING

In order to collect bird, mammal, fish, or reptile specimens successfully for mounting or for the preparation of "study-skins," it is necessary, first, to make a thorough study of the wildlife in the area in which the hunting is done, and, second, to acquire a knowledge of how to take care of the specimens after they are collected. Most important of all, one must be sure to skin, clean, and preserve the skins of all specimens as quickly as possible; otherwise they are sure to spoil and thus be of little value for mounting purposes.

The introductions to each of the following chapters contain directions for the proper care of the specimens, whether they be birds, animals, fish, or reptiles, before they are prepared or mounted. One can never give too much attention to the care of specimens in the field since the more damaged the specimen, the more difficult it will be to mount in a lifelike and natural position or prepare as a study-skin.

It is extremely important to remember, in addition, that all wildlife is protected by state and federal laws. One cannot go into the field at one's pleasure and collect natural history specimens. Songbirds are protected at all times and those birds, animals, and fish which are listed as game are protected by state game laws. Songbirds can only be taken with the approval of the Fish and Wildlife Service, U. S. Department of the Interior, Washington, D. C. This Department issues federal permits allowing the collection of certain non-game birds in restricted localities, but such permits are issued only for the purposes of scientific study. To hunt game animals, one must abide by the laws of the state regulating the number and kinds of animals which can be taken in a particular season.

Care of Specimens in the Field

There are certain rules to be observed after the specimens are collected in the field. When collecting birds, pick up the bird by the feet as soon as it is secured and gently shake it a few times. This will make the feathers fall back into position. Wipe off bloodstains and dirt from the plumage with a small wad of absorbent cotton, and plug any large shot holes, the vent, and throat with cotton to prevent blood and stomach juices from running out over the feathers. If the eyes are damaged, wipe out and place a small piece of cotton over each eye. Smooth and adjust the plumage and roll the bird in newspaper before putting it away in the shooting bag or coat pocket. This precaution will keep the feathers from becoming disarranged and broken.

One does not have to be so careful with animals, since, in most cases, the hair will not break off or be damaged as easily as will the feathers of birds. Bloodstains and dirt should be wiped off the hair and all large shot holes plugged; bloodstains are much easier to remove when fresh than after they have dried.

With all specimens, and especially with fish and reptiles, color notes of the fleshy parts, such as the bare skin around the face, eyelids, legs, and feet, and the color of the eyes should be recorded. When collecting fish and reptiles for mounting, the colors of all parts of the body must be noted at once since these colors start to fade as soon as the specimens are dead. It is not important which method of recording colors is used. What is important is that one have a record of these colors to refer to later when restoring colors to the faded parts in the mounted specimen. If experienced with colors, one can make a sketch of the face and legs of the animal or bird, or an outline of the fish, and fill in the correct colors on this outline with crayons, water, or oil colors. When collecting in the field, however, the use of crayons, and simply marking in the colors, will prove easiest.

Skinning Specimens for Study-Skins

The proper methods of skinning birds and mammals are discussed at length in other chapters. Fish and reptiles collected for study purposes should immediately be placed in metal containers filled with the preserving solution Formula #101 (see Chapter 4). Back in the workshop, the specimens should be transferred from the metal containers to glass ones so that they can be inspected without being removed from the solution. As far as it is possible, they should always be covered with the preserving solution.

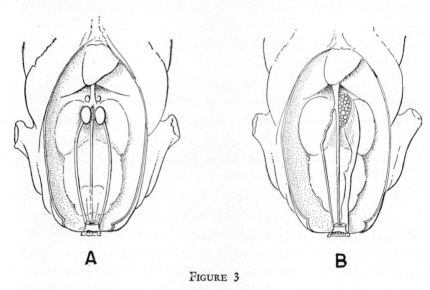

A   B

FIGURE 3

Sex Identification

When collecting specimens for study-skins, it is very important to identify the sex of each specimen on the label. This is easy to do with mammals, but not so easy with some species of birds, particularly at certain seasons of the year. It is sometimes necessary to examine the bird internally. To do this, skin the bird, lay the body on its back, and carefully cut through the left side of the abdominal wall from the vent to a point just beyond the forward edge of the left thigh. Press aside the thigh and

mass of intestines and the sex organs that lie close to the back-
bone will be exposed. Figure 3, A, shows the sex organs of the
male bird; 3, B, the female.

Making Study-Skins

After the bird has been skinned (see Chapter 5), and all
flesh cleaned from tail butt, leg and wing bones, and skull, the
skin is preserved. For both bird and mammal study-skins, the

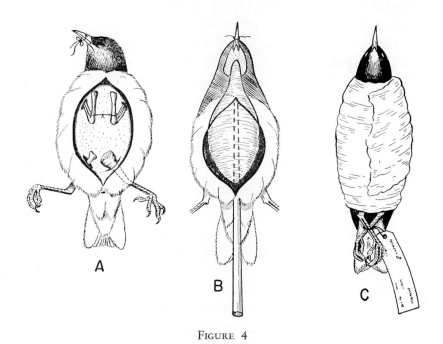

A

B

C

FIGURE 4

powdered borax that was used to skin the specimens will act as
a preservative. Just be sure that all parts of the skin are well
covered. The bill is tied together with thread and a small wad
of cotton is inserted into the throat and into each eye socket.
Tie the wings together as close as possible without breaking any
bones.

Wrap cotton around each leg bone to replace the leg muscles
cut away. These steps are illustrated in Figure 4, A.

Next secure a small stick, thin at one end and longer than the bird. Beginning at the tip (the part that will enter the bird's skull), wrap on cotton, twirling the stick counterclockwise in order to build up a cotton body having the same shape and size as the natural body and neck which were removed. Insert the smaller end—the neck part—firmly into the skull cavity and adjust the skin and feathers around the cotton body. The bird can be held up by the stick and the skin and feathers easily adjusted and smoothed into place, as shown in Figure 4, B. Care should be exercised at this point not to stretch the skin.

The skin is now brought together, starting at the vent and working toward the head, and held by a few loose stitches. The legs are crossed and tied together with the label cord, the wings adjusted into position, and the finished skin wrapped in a layer of cotton or cheesecloth until the specimen is dry. The stick is now removed by twisting in a clockwise direction and sliding it from the cotton body. Care must be exercised in both skinning and filling up the skin not to stretch it in any way. This precaution applies especially with regard to the neck; do not have the neck too long. It is well to unwrap the study-skin the next day to make sure the wings and feather pattern are in their proper positions and smooth. The finished study-skin is illustrated in Figure 4, C.

In making up study-skins of mammals, the skull is carefully removed, cleaned, and kept separate from the skin. Skulls are boxed and kept with the study-skins since mammal skulls are important in identification and study.

After removing the animal's body and cleaning all flesh and fat from the skin and leg bones (see Chapter 6), preserve the skin by rubbing on powdered borax. (Should the skin dry out, dampen before rubbing on the borax so that it will be absorbed.) Take one or two stitches through the lips to hold them together, and wrap either cotton or fine tow around each of the four leg bones to replace the flesh. Wrap with cotton a thin wire longer than the tail and insert it in the tail skin clear to the tip (Figure 5, A). This will replace the tail bone and flesh.

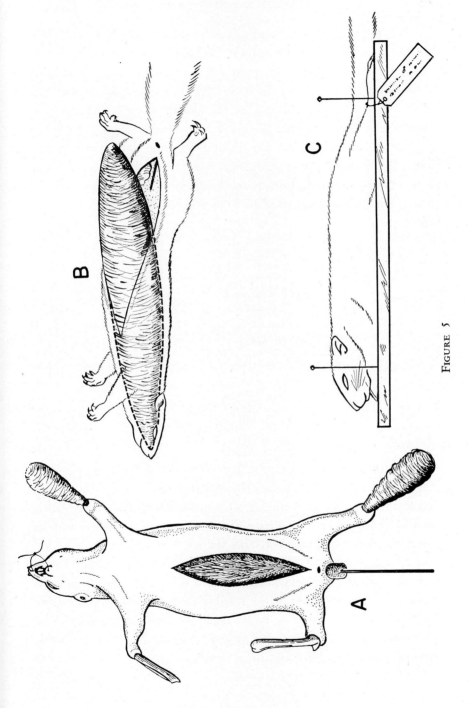

FIGURE 5

13

Next, the skin, legs, and tail are turned right side out. An artificial body, made of loosely-wrapped tow and about the shape and size of the one removed, is inserted into the skin as shown in Figure 5, B, to fill it out from head to tail. (The tail wire lays along the bottom of the body filling.) The skin is now sewed together with a very fine thread.

Mammal study-skins are pinned on any flat surface until dry. They should be placed belly down with the front and rear legs securely pinned close to the body and the head and tail in a straight line as illustrated in Figure 5, C. The label is tied to the right foot.

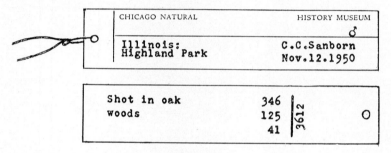

FIGURE 6

Recording Information

It is important to mention here that no scientific study-skin has any value, no matter how beautiful a specimen or how well made a skin, unless it is labeled with complete data. These labels should show the place where the specimen was collected, the date, the name of collector, and the sex (male indicated by ♂, the female by ♀). Color notations, the collector's field number, and other descriptive information should also be noted. In the case of mammal skins, the total length and the length of the tail and of the hind foot from heel to longest claw should be measured in millimeters and noted. Figure 6 shows a sample museum field label for mammal study-skins.

Chapter 3

TOOLS AND MATERIALS

The tools used in taxidermy are relatively few and simple; the materials needed are easy to secure and inexpensive. As in all work, the more specialized tools one has to work with, the easier and less complicated the task. With only a few simple tools and the directions given in this book, however, one can turn out fine examples of taxidermy; for which tools and materials one uses is not so important as possessing a thorough knowledge of the subjects. One should study wildlife so that lifelike, characteristic poses can be given the mounted specimens. After one has learned the techniques and knows the subjects, he needs only hard work and experience to become a good workman in this field.

One should always use good tools; they are better and will last longer than cheap ones and are, therefore, a good investment. A few of the tools needed are of special design and may have to be made by the preparator. Some of the tools needed, however, can be purchased under another name; a curved grapefruit knife, for example, available in any 5-and-10-cent store, makes an excellent skin scraper for bird and small animal skins. How to make special tools needed in the tanning of skins is explained in Chapter 9.

Today, as was not true in past years, many necessary materials can be purchased. It is much easier and cheaper to purchase materials ready for use than to mix them and run the risk of not having the proper proportions.

As one achieves a mastery of the techniques, he may want to add more tools to the following list or, possibly, to substitute some other tools for those given. The list, however, is complete for all work.

Tools:

1 surgeon's small scalpel
1 surgeon's medium-sized scalpel
1 kitchen paring knife
1 butcher's skinning knife
1 pocketknife
1 toothed grapefruit knife, curved at the end
1 pair of surgeon's heavy bone cutters
1 medium-sized carborundum stone
1 pair of straight forceps (5″), with long, slender tips
1 pair of straight forceps (7″), with blunt tips
1 pair of straight forceps (10″), with blunt tips
1 pair of small surgical scissors, with straight tips
1 pair of medium-sized surgical scissors, having one blunt blade
1 package of sewing needles, assorted sizes
4 boxes of brass pins, assorted sizes
1 package of three-cornered, curved needles, assorted sizes
1 tape measure (linen); approximately 25 feet in length
2 toothbrushes, different sizes
1 claw hammer
1 tack hammer
1 ripsaw; 1 hack saw; 1 coping saw
1 pair of heavy common shears
1 pair of medium-sized tinner's shears
1 small Bernard side-cutting pliers
1 medium-sized Bernard side-cutting pliers
1 small pointed-nose pliers
1 medium-sized blunt-nose pliers
1 drill set
3 mill files, assorted sizes
1 medium-sized wood rasp
1 coarse wood rasp
1 tap and die (thread-cutting set); $\frac{3}{16}$-inch to $\frac{1}{2}$-inch dies
1 small trowel
1 spatula
3 modeling tools, assorted sizes
1 coarse steel furrier's comb
1 set of artist's bristle brushes, assorted sizes
1 set of artist's oil colors
1 nest of crockery mixing bowls
1 double boiler, 1-quart size

MATERIALS:

Excelsior, or wood-wool, coarse grade
Tow, fine grade
Cotton batting, long-fiber grade
Absorbent cotton
Jeweler's cotton
Balsa wood
Powdered borax
White cornmeal
Plaster of Paris
Salt, medium and coarse grade
Carpenter's glue
Modeling clay
Papier-mâché
Sulphonated neat's-foot oil

Petroleum wax, yellow
Potato starch
Oilcloth, cheap grade, several yards
Cheesecloth, coarse grade
Annealed, galvanized wire, assorted sizes
Hardware cloth (galvanized wire netting), ¼-inch to ½-inch mesh
Glass eyes, best grade for the taxidermy trade
Cotton and linen thread, assorted
Ball, or store, twine
Cotton "cops"
Notebook, pencils, and labels

SUPPLY COMPANIES:

Central Scientific Company, Chicago, Ill.
Jonas Brothers, Denver, Colo.
Favor Ruhl & Company, Inc., Chicago, Ill.
American Excelsior Corporation, Chicago, Ill.
Shavings & Sawdust Company, Chicago, Ill.
McKesson & Robbins, Inc., Chicago, Ill.
Dennison Manufacturing Company, Chicago, Ill.
American Balsa-Wood Company, Newark, N. J.
Western Stoneware Company, Chicago, Ill.
Arthur C. Trask Company, Chicago, Ill.

Chapter 4

FORMULAS

One must be careful in purchasing and mixing solutions. Substitutions should not be made unless specified. Most of the materials used in the different preparations needed in taxidermy can be purchased from local drug or department stores, and all can be secured from any of the firms that supply taxidermy materials.

The following chapters will refer to several formulas needed in taxidermy work by the numbers assigned them in the following list.

#101, PRESERVING SOLUTION (specimens):

Water	15 parts
Commercial formaldehyde	1 part

Use only commercial formaldehyde (40%). Mix it with water in the given ratio. Keep the solution tightly closed in a glass or metal container.

#102, DEGREASING SOLUTION: (This should never be used by amateurs indoors and no flame should ever come near the solution.)

Benzine	8 parts
Commercial alcohol	2 parts

Mix together. Keep tightly closed in a glass container when not in use. *Do not* leave uncovered. When it has been used, pour off the clear solution from grease which settles in the bottom.

#103, PRESERVING SOLUTION (mounts):

Water	1 gallon
Sodium arsenite	1 ounce

Warm water, then add sodium arsenite and stir until thoroughly dissolved. Keep covered in a glass container. *Note:* This solution is poisonous and should be labeled *"POISON. Handle with extreme caution."*

BORAX PRESERVING SOLUTION:

Water	1 gallon
Powdered borax	4 ounces

Stir the water while adding the borax until it is thoroughly dissolved. This solution can be used over and over until dirty and is recommended for all amateur work. It is safer to use than any other preserving solution.

#104, CARBOLIC-ACID SOLUTION:

Water	1 gallon
Carbolic acid	1½ tablespoonfuls

Use carbolic-acid crystals and dissolve them according to directions on bottle. Mix solution only as needed.

#105, MODELING COMPOSITION:

See Formula #106

To the body paste, add ground asbestos, whiting, or other similar fiber. Work this into the paste a little at a time. Consistency of composition can be controlled by the amount of fiber added.

#106, BODY PASTE:

Dextrin	5 pounds
Glycerine	6 ounces
Carbolic acid	2 teaspoonfuls
Arsenic water	2 tablespoonfuls

Use a 2- or 3-gallon crock for mixing. Bring water to a boil. Pour into the crock about 2 inches of boiling water, then add glycerine, carbolic acid, and arsenic water, and mix well. Add dextrin, a little at a time, stirring the mixture until it is smooth. Add more boiling water, mixing gradually until the solution is the consistency of thin glue. *Note:* Use only British Standard Gum Dextrin, #160.

#107, MODELING WAX:

Beeswax	3 parts
Rosin	1 part

Use only pure white beeswax. Melt both in separate containers in a hot water bath. Mix together while in liquid state, then pour into small molds to cool.

#108, OILING SOLUTION:

Turpentine	3 parts
Linseed oil	1 part

Mix together. Shake well each time used.

#109, ALUM-WATER SOLUTION:

Water	1 gallon
Alum	1 teaspoonful

Mix water and alum together, stirring until alum is dissolved. Mix enough solution for each job as needed.

#110, FLEXIBLE GLUE:

Glue	9 parts
Glycerine	1 part

Melt glue in a water bath, having it very thin. Add glycerine and mix thoroughly. Each time solution is melted, stir well before using it again.

#111, PICKLE SOLUTION:

Water	1 gallon
Salt	½ pound
Sulphuric acid	1 ½ ounces

Add the salt to warm water and stir until thoroughly dissolved. Then add the sulphuric acid. Allow the solution to cool before use. Keep in a wood or glass container—never in metal.

#112, SULPHONATED NEAT'S-FOOT OIL SOLUTION:

Water	1 part
Sulphonated neat's-foot oil	1 part

Add the sulphonated oil to warm water and mix thoroughly. Warm the solution each time before use.

#113, ALUM SOLUTION:

Water	1 gallon
Salt	½ pound
Alum	¼ pound
Carbolic acid	½ ounce

Add the carbolic acid to warm water and mix well. Add all other ingredients and stir thoroughly. This solution can be used over and over by the addition of a small amount of salt and alum each time.

#114, DEHAIRING SOLUTION:

Water	1 gallon
Hydrated lime	1/4 pound
Red arsenic	pinch

Mix the lime and arsenic together with a small amount of water to form a paste. Add this to the water, mixing thoroughly. Make enough of the solution at one time to cover the skin. *Note:* This mixture is poisonous; label it *Poison*.

#115, NEUTRALIZING SOLUTION:

Water	1 gallon
Boric acid	1 ounce

Add the boric acid to warm water and stir until dissolved. Mix as desired for use.

#116, LIMEWATER SOLUTION:

Water	1 gallon
Slaked lime	3 ounces

Warm the water. Add the lime and mix thoroughly until dissolved.

#117, ALUM SALT SOLUTION:

Water	1 gallon
Salt	3 ounces
Chrome alum	15 grams

Add the salt to warm water and mix well. Add the alum and stir until dissolved. Keep in a glass container.

Chapter 5

BIRDS

One's first attempt in taxidermy is usually the mounting of a bird since it is fairly easy to skin most birds and mount them in a lifelike position. Keep in mind, however, that successful work with birds requires more knowledge of the positions birds take than of the many different mounting techniques in use today. One should make a thorough study of the bird's characteristic poses since it is the final result, not the methods or techniques used, that counts.

Preliminary Steps

For the first attempt, select a specimen in perfect condition; the more damaged the bird, the harder it will be to make it look alive. Handle the specimen carefully, taking care not to disturb the feather pattern; once the feathers are broken, they cannot be pulled together. Plug all shot holes, mouth, nostrils, and vent with cotton, and immediately wipe or wash off all blood from the plumage with a pad of cotton dipped into a weak solution of ammonia and cold water. Be sure to remove all bloodstains at this time; if left to harden they are sometimes impossible to wash off completely.

Color Notes and Contact Outline

After the bird is collected, accurate color notes should be made of the bill, eyes, legs and feet, and any fleshy parts. This must be done while the bird is still warm, since these colors will fade quickly. Color notes can be made with a wax crayon, oil or water colors, or by simply naming the colors on a penciled outline. Any method will suffice; color notes are made only as a guide to follow later when the colors are restored to the mounted bird to bring back the correct colors to the faded parts. At this time, it will help if several contact outlines are made of the bird. Lay it on its side on a piece of heavy, plain paper, and shape it into several positions. The specimen will take on a lifelike pose while limp and before being skinned. Trace around the body, making several different outlines to refer to later when deciding the position of the mount.

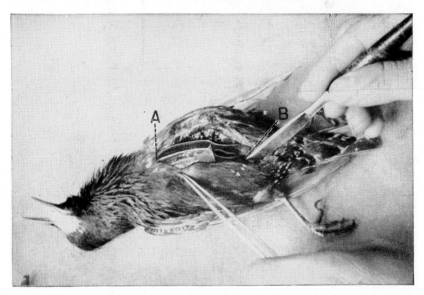

FIGURE 7

Skinning

Lay the specimen on its back, head to the left. Part the feathers along the breastbone with the fingers; a bare strip of skin shows here in most birds. The opening cut is made along breastbone, line *A–B* in Figure 7, using a small, sharp scalpel. Do not cut through the abdominal wall or blood and body fluids will run out onto the feathers. Sift powdered borax into the opening cut and on the skin as you work. If the meat of the bird is wanted for eating, however, *do not* use borax. Instead, sift on corn meal to absorb the blood and fluids. Later, when

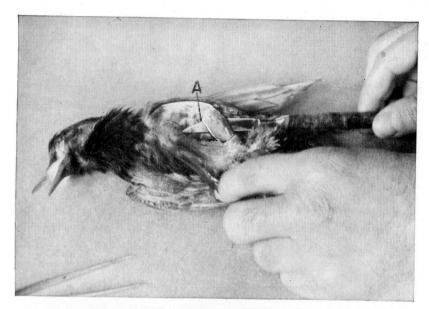

FIGURE 8

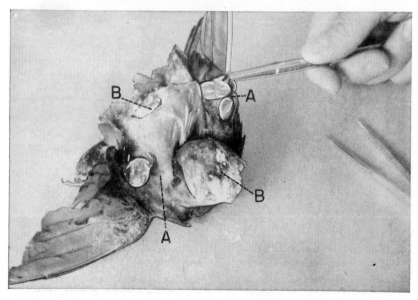

FIGURE 9

24

the meat to be consumed has been removed, be sure to rub borax over the inside of the skin.

Working down each side of the body toward the tail, separate the skin from the body with the fingers and scalpel. When the legs are reached, grasp each from the outside, force upward, and detach from the body at *A* in Figure 8. Do not cut through, or break the bones, but detach them at the joint.

FIGURE 10

Work the skin off down to the tail and detach it, taking care not to cut too close to the tail feathers. If the skin is cut too close, these feathers will fall out. The legs are detached at *A*, and *B* in Figure 9 shows where the tail is cut from the body.

Continue working the skin down over the back, sifting on borax, until the wings are reached, *A* in Figure 10. Separate both wings from the body at the ball and socket joint. Do not cut, or break the bone. Use care in removing the skin and do not stretch it in any way. This precaution must be observed especially when working with the neck skin.

Work the skin down over neck and head. Use extreme care when the ears are reached, pulling the entire ear lining from the head with a small pair of tweezers. Also, be careful not to cut or tear the skin around the eyes and lips. Skin down to the bill, shown at *A* in Figure 11. With small birds, leave the skin attached to the bill. The body then is separated from the skin at base of the skull, *B*, leaving the skull attached to the skin. The brain can now be removed from the brain cavity.

FIGURE 11

Some birds have heads so large that the neck skin cannot be pulled over the skull. With these birds, cut off the neck at base of the skull and turn the head and neck skin right side out by making a cut on top of the head, *A-B* in Figure 12. Now skin and clean out the skull in the usual manner.

Figure 13 shows the skin removed and turned wrong side out. It must now be thoroughly cleaned. Remove all flesh from around base of tail, *A*. Cut away all flesh from the leg bones, *B*, and wing bones, *C*. Remove the eyes and brain, cut

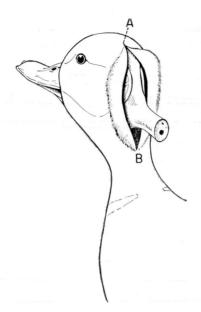

FIGURE 12

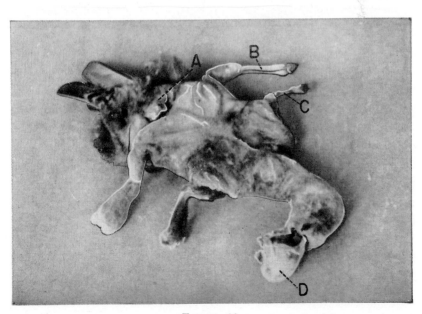

FIGURE 13

away the face muscles, and clean the skull, *D*. Leave only the small muscles to hold the upper and lower bill together.

When birds with large wings are skinned, the flesh must be removed from the underside of each wing. Cut along the line shown as *A–B* in Figure 14, and remove all flesh and wing muscles from the bones through this opening. If the bird is to be mounted in a flying position, care must be exercised in making this cut and removing the flesh. Later, the wing must be wired and the opening sewed together in such a manner that the incision will not show.

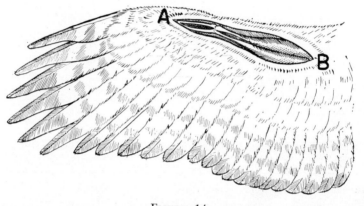

FIGURE 14

In all large birds and those with fleshy legs and feet, the tendons must be removed. Cut open the pads on the bottom of each foot and under each toe. Insert a knife handle or similar tool under each tendon, *A* in Figure 15, and pull it out. The tendons cannot be removed, however, until the flesh on the leg bones has been cut away.

Care of the Skin

The skin must now be scraped with a small skin scraper. One may use a grapefruit knife or a dull knife. All fat and inner skin muscles which still adhere must be removed. Scrape

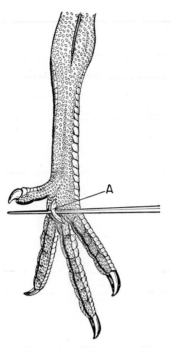

FIGURE 15

where the butts of the feathers protrude through the skin (called "feather tracts"). Work off all fat and flesh until these "tracts" are clean. This part of the work is most important and care must be exercised not to cut or tear the skin. Insert a small pad of cotton into each eye cavity and turn the skin right side out. Immediately adjust the feathers on the head and neck which have become disarranged.

It will now have to be washed and degreased to remove all remaining dirt or bloodstains or fat. Used mild soap flakes and lukewarm water, working up the suds in enough water to wash the specimen thoroughly. Work the skin in this with the hands until it is clean, then rinse in several changes of cold water until all the soap is removed. This is important; if all the soapy water is not washed from the skin the feathers will not "fluff" and look natural when the bird is mounted. After it is rinsed,

drain the skin between newspapers, changing them as they become soaked, until all excess water has drained off.

Now put the skin through a degreasing solution, Formula
#102, to make the feathers clean and "fluffy." Work the skin
in this solution until all grease is out, and then dry it in fine hardwood sawdust. Some birds, such as hawks, owls, and grouse,
must be dried in plaster of Paris. In such cases, be careful not
to put the skin in the plaster until all water is out of it.
Shake out the sawdust or plaster, and dry and "fluff" the feathers with compressed air if it is obtainable. A small stick or bam-
boo rattan can also be used to gently beat out the sawdust or
plaster, but nothing can compare to compressed air. Next, adjust the feather pattern in place and smooth all the body feathers. After the skin has been cleaned, it must be poisoned with
the preserving solution, Formula #103. Brush this solution
cover the inside of the skin, skull, and wings, and on the legs and
feet, making sure that all parts are thoroughly covered. Should
the skin dry out before the body is made, dampen it with
a carbolic acid-water solution, Formula #104, until it is
relaxed.

Mounting

Annealed, galvanized wires are used to support the bird.
The size and length of these wires depend upon the specimen
being mounted. In all cases, they should be strong enough to
support the mounted bird.

Using the natural body, A in Figure 16, as a guide, model an
artificial body from fine, dampened excelsior, winding about it
strong thread, or string, B, to keep it in shape. One with
enough skill can carve a body from balsa wood, following the
outline drawings to get the exact size and shape of the natural
body. The neck and body wire is run through the artificial
body and securely anchored by clinching it into the body.
Measure the length and size of the natural neck removed. Rub
wax on the neck wire, then build it up to the correct size with
jeweler's cotton, winding it slowly between the fingers. Mold

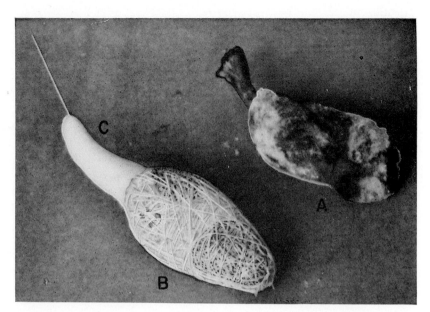

FIGURE 16

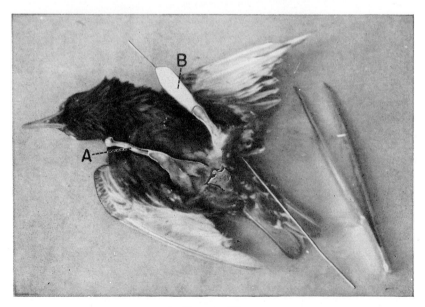

FIGURE 17

on extra cotton (the amount depending upon the size of the bird), at C to enter the skull.

The legs are wired by inserting wires up inside each leg and along the leg bone, starting from the outside and at the bottom of the foot. Wrap jeweler's cotton around both the wire and the leg bone to take the place of the flesh that was cut away. The leg bone before wiring is shown at A in Figure 17. The wired bone with leg muscles replaced with cotton is shown at B.

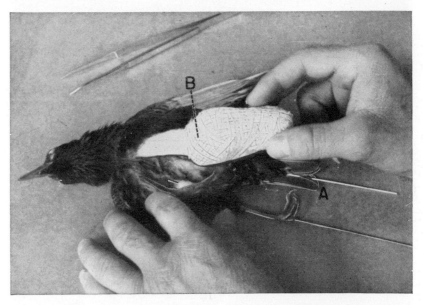

FIGURE 18

Wire the tail by running a wire through the base of the feathers (A in Figure 18). Work the artificial body and neck, B, up inside the neck skin. (The neck wire is pushed up through the neck, into the skull, and out the top of head.) Now carefully adjust and fit the skin to the body, shaking it from time to time so the feathers will fall into place.

Anchor all wires securely in their proper positions. The tail wire is anchored at A in Figure 19; leg wires at B, the wings will be fastened in place later at C. and the neck wire fixed at

D. After all wires are securely anchored, begin at the vent and sew the skin together toward the breastbone. Do not catch any feathers in sewing. Now lift the bird by its feet and shake it several times to loosen the feathers and make them fall into place.

FIGURE 19

The specimen is now fastened to its perch or base by the wires left protruding from the bottom of the feet. Do not pull the feet down tightly to the perch or the mount will look flat-footed. Bend the neck, wings, legs, and tail, shaping the specimen into a lifelike position, and arrange all feathers in place. Fill out the throat cavity with a small wad of cotton and pin or tie the bill together with thread. Fasten the toes to the perch with pins or soft wax and spread the tail feathers, holding them in position until dry with two strips of cardboard pinned together. The wings can be fixed in place with wires or, if the bird is small, with pins. While eyelids are still relaxed, fill in the eye sockets with papier-mâché and set in place glass eyes

of the proper size and color. Adjust the eyelids to give expression to the face. Tie down the feathers with soft, fine thread or
string to hold them in place until the mount is dry (Figures
20 and 21).

FIGURE 20

Allow the mount to dry for several weeks, depending on its
size and the climate. While it is drying, check from time to
time to adjust the feathers. When it is dry, remove all pins,
thread, string, and cardboard, and cut off protruding wires.
Refer to the color notes and restore the proper colors to the
bill, eyes, legs and feet, and all other fleshy parts that have
faded. Use oil paints thinned with turpentine and a little linseed oil for this work. Do not apply the colors too thickly or
these parts will have a painted, unnatural look that should be
avoided.

Figure 22 shows two well-mounted specimens.

FIGURE 21

FIGURE 22

Mounting Large Birds

Skin the specimen, leaving the legs and skull attached to the body (Figure 23). The opening incision is made in the same way as in smaller birds, but when the legs are reached, the skin is cut open inside of each leg. The tail and wings are left attached to the skin. When the skull is reached, the head skin is carefully cut away by detaching it at the bill. After removing the skin, wash, degrease, and dry it, then poison and keep it wrapped in several cloths dampened with the carbolic acid-water solution, Formula #104. These cloths should be kept damp so that the skin will not dry while the artificial body is being modeled.

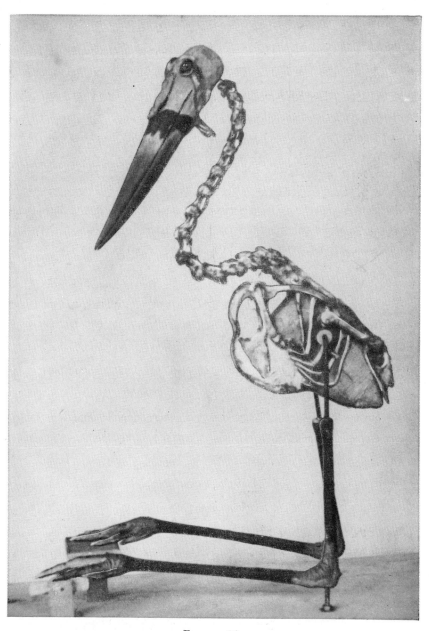

FIGURE 23

Make a contact outline of the natural body and take several measurements at different places. Cut away the flesh and muscles, and remove the viscera. Do not detach any part of the skeleton, but leave all bones held together by the ligaments. The skeleton is now washed in cold, running water to remove all blood and fluids.

From a piece of balsa wood, shape a core to fit into the stomach cavity in the skeleton; in this will be anchored the wires and rods which will support the specimen. Shellac this wood core before placing it in the skeleton. To support the mount, run wires or iron rods of the proper size up through the legs and anchor them in the core. Fasten the neck in a similar manner by running a wire through the skull down through the vertebrae of the neck and into the core. Shape the skeleton in position and anchor it to the base by the leg rods. Brush formaldehyde over the entire skeleton and allow the bones to set. Be sure the skeleton is posed in the position you want the mount to have; this position cannot be changed once the skeleton has set.

Next, work out all details of the size and shape of the body. Use papier-mâché to model on the flesh that was cut away from the skeleton (Figure 24). With this material, build up the anatomy a little at a time, allowing each layer to dry thoroughly before adding another. After the body has been modeled to conform to the measurements of the natural body, let the form dry completely. This will take several weeks for a large bird. When it has finally dried, give the artificial body a coat of shellac to make it waterproof.

The skin, which has been kept relaxed, is now pulled over the form and carefully adjusted into place (Figure 25). The head skin is held in place with pins, the wings and tail supported with wires, and all incisions sewed together. After the skin has dried to the form, the plumage is adjusted and the colors restored in the usual manner.

Figure 24

39

FIGURE 25

Wiring Wings

The wings of all large birds, and those to be mounted in a flying position, must be wired first and then anchored to the artificial body. Sharpen one end of the wing wire, *A* in Figure 26, bend the opposite end around and place it along the wing bone, *B*, and tie securely in place. Wind fine tow or jeweler's cotton around the wire and bone, *C*, to replace the wing muscles cut away. Anchor it to the body by the same method used to wire the legs in position.

When the bird is to be mounted in a flying position, the wings must be wired in a different manner. Use a wire heavy enough to support the spread wings, cut it to the proper length, and

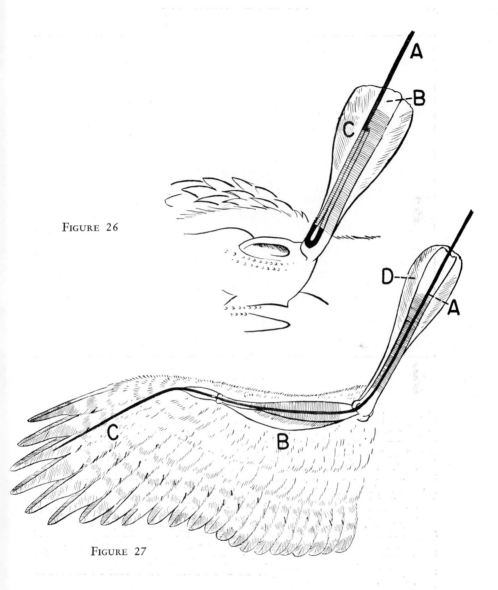

Figure 26

Figure 27

FIGURE 28

sharpen it on both ends. Place in position along the wing bones, *A* and *B* in Figure 27. Then force it along into the base of the third primary feather, *C*. Tie the wire securely to the bone and wind on tow or cotton, *D*, to replace the muscles. The wings are then anchored to the artificial body.

Figure 28 shows a flying bird, a kingfisher, with the wings supported in position with heavy wires. Figure 29 illustrates an outstanding habitat group. Wild turkeys are shown in an autumn setting; an example of the combined work of museum taxidermists and artists.

FIGURE 29

43

Chapter 6

MAMMALS

When mounting an animal, first select a position or pose that is characteristic of that particular animal, and easy to work out. The techniques and formulas of taxidermy can be learned easily and quickly, but it will take years of studying animals in their natural habitats, then more years of experience in copying these poses to achieve perfectly lifelike positions in mounted animals.

Preliminary Steps

As soon as the animal is collected, wipe off all blood and body juices or fluids from the hair. If shot holes are large enough to allow blood to seep out, plug them with cotton or grasses. The skins of animals larger than squirrels or rabbits must be tanned before mounting (see Chapter 9), but smaller skins can be treated according to the methods given here.

It will be of help later if several contact outlines can be made of the animal before and after skinning. Lay the specimen on its side on a sheet of plain paper, and pose it in the position you want the mount to have. Trace around the body with a pencil. Accurate measurements are taken over all parts of the body after the skin is removed, and these measurements indicated in their proper places on the outline.

Skinning

Lay the animal on its back, head to your left, as shown in Figure 30. The opening incision, A–B, is made with a sharp scalpel or knife from a point between the front legs to a point between the hind legs. Use care not to cut through the abdominal wall, or blood and body fluids will run out.

44

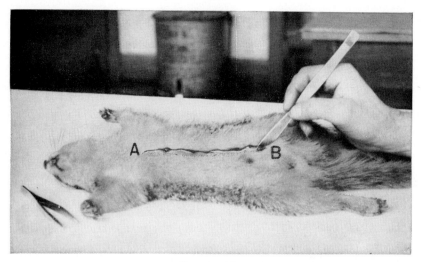

FIGURE 30

Cut skin loose from the body by working down each side, using fingers and scalpel, until the legs are reached. Then work the skin down over the legs as shown in Figure 31, *A*. Skin out the legs down to the toes; it will help in some cases if a cut is made on the bottom of each foot. Now separate each toe and cut off the leg and foot, leaving the foot, *B*, attached to the skin.

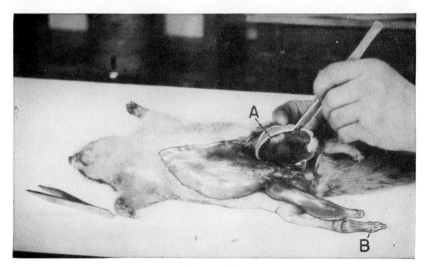

FIGURE 31

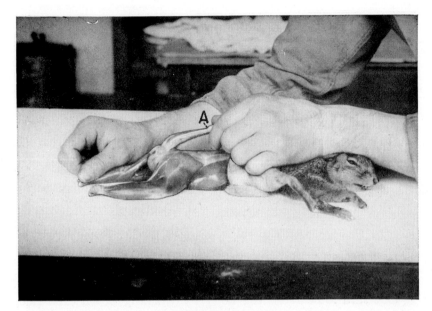

FIGURE 32

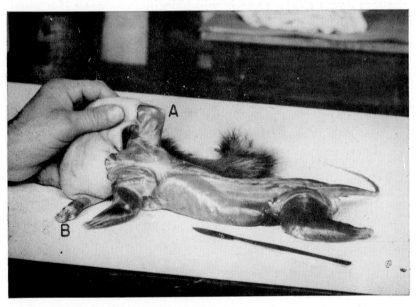

FIGURE 33

46

Make a small cut on the underside an inch from the tip of the tail. Cut the skin from around the tail butt and grasp it with the fingers of one hand. Hold the animal with the other hand, as shown at *A* in Figure 32, and remove the tail. Be sure to remove the entire tail skin.

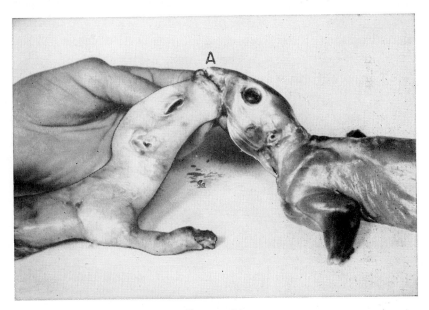

FIGURE 34

Continue skinning down over the back, using the scalpel, until the front legs, shown at *A* in Figure 33, are reached. Skin out both front legs as was done with the rear ones, leaving the feet attached to the skin, *B*.

Care must be exercised to cut close to the skull when skinning out the head, especially around ears and eyes. In large animals, the ear cartilage will have to be removed (see Chapter 8). When the lips, *A* in Figure 34, are reached, skin these away from the teeth taking care not to cut the lip skin. Cut the end of the nose close to the skull so that the nostrils will remain on the skin. Remove the skin entirely from the body.

Care of the Skin

After the skin is removed from the body, it should be washed in cold, running water until all blood and dirt have been removed. It is then immersed in commercial grain alcohol, which "sets" it. Keep this alcohol in a glass, not a metal, container. For an animal the size of the one illustrated, leave the skin immersed overnight and keep the container well covered. When the skin is removed from the alcohol, use the fleshing knives (see Chapter 9) to scrape it. Breaking up all fibers and skin muscles will give the skin suppleness. Shave down around the base of the ears and remove the cartilage from around the nostrils. Split open the lips and eyelids. Cut away all flesh from the feet and toes. Now poison the skin with the preserving solution, Formula #103. After this solution is brushed over the flesh side of the skin, roll the skin up, flesh side in, and lay it away until the artificial body is made. Do not let the skin get dry, but keep it relaxed until ready to be pulled over the body form. If necessary, dampen with carbolic acid-water solution (#104).

Mounting

Several methods are used in the mounting of small mammals but the one given will prove easiest for the beginner and enable him to produce a mount which is a faithful copy of a lifelike position of the animal. In "setting up" an animal, particularly a large one, make certain it is balanced correctly on all four legs in the position in which it is posed.

Following the measurements, contact outlines, and other data taken before and after skinning the animal, both the skull and body can be shaped in balsa wood (Figure 35). By another method, the natural skull is saved and cleaned of all flesh and the eyes, tongue, and brain removed. The skull then is anchored to the artificial body with a wire.

When carving the body from the balsa wood, start with a piece of wood larger than the dimensions of the natural body. Then, with a small coping saw and a sharp knife, an artificial body can be carved and shaped from the balsa block to an exact copy of the natural one. By copying the contact outlines when carving, the artificial body can be given a characteristic pose. Cut away sections for the front and hind legs and bore a small hole at *A* through the form for the leg wires. Lips, nostrils, and eye sockets are carved in detail. Glass eyes of the proper color and size are set in position with papier-mâché at *B*. Now shellac the entire form to waterproof it.

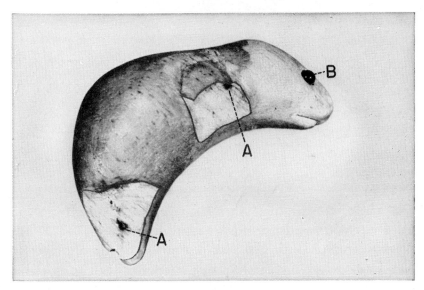

FIGURE 35

Again using previous measurements and drawing to determine the required length of the wires and the outline of the legs, shape the leg wires to the natural bend of the leg bones. First, rub wax on the wires, then build up each leg by wrapping on fine tow held in place with thread until the exact size and shape of the leg is achieved (Figure 36). With an animal the size of the one illustrated, allow approximately four inches of wire to extend beyond the bottom of each foot. Anchor each leg to the balsa wood body at *A*. In the same manner, build up the tail wire with tow or jeweler's cotton until it is approximately natural size, and then anchor it to the body at *B*.

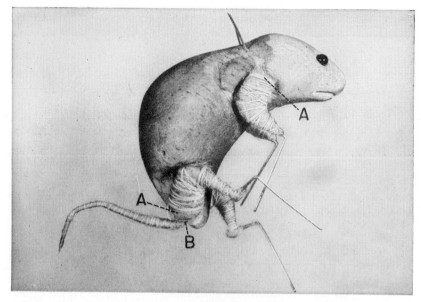

FIGURE 36

Depressions in the body where the legs and tail are joined, and where the natural skull, if used, anchors to the form, are filled out with modeling composition, Formula #105. A roll of this composition is also placed around the lips and eyes to help in modeling the correct facial expression and to hold the skin in place. A small wad of the composition is worked down each leg skin to the foot, and the skull, legs, and tail are covered with thin body paste (Formula #106). The skin is now pulled over the form and carefully adjusted and worked into place (Figure 37). Keep the skin relaxed while working by wrapping it in damp carbolic acid-water cloths. Sew the incision together.

Drill holes in the base or tree branch to receive all leg wires and fasten the mount by anchoring these wires. Spread and pin the toes in place. Shape the animal to the position wanted by turning the head or body. Model the eyelids and pin the corners of the eyes with small pins to hold them in position.

The lips and nostrils are modeled and the lips also held in place with small pins. The ears can be held up with small sections of cardboard until dry. Comb and brush the hair until smooth, and complete the process of shaping the animal. Drying will take several weeks, depending on size of animal and the climate.

FIGURE 37

After the animal is thoroughly dry, remove all pins, wires, and cardboards, and cut off all protruding wires that show. Again, brush and comb the hair of the tail to "fluff" it out. (It is best to do this while the animal is drying, however.) Clean off all traces of composition from around the lips and eyes, and wax the eyelids and the inside of the lips (Formula #107). Restore natural color to the skin around the eyes, lips, and nostrils with oil colors following the color notes taken when the specimen was fresh. Figure 38 shows a well-mounted specimen.

FIGURE 38

Large Mammals

After the skin of a large mammal is removed from the body, it is absolutely necessary that it be thoroughly covered with salt. When this has been done, roll up the skin, flesh side in, and lay it away in a cool place—never in the sun or near heat. Next day, unroll it, shake off the excess salt, and salt it again. Roll up once more, flesh side in, and ship it to the tanner at once. (All large mammal skins must be tanned before mounting. See Chapter 9 for tanning instructions.) Contact outlines and numerous measurements of the important parts of the body such as the face and legs are taken in several places and recorded. These data will prove of great help when the job of mounting is begun.

The incisions necessary are plotted in dotted lines in Figure 39. The opening cut is made from a point between the front legs, A, to a point between the hind legs, B. Split the skin open to the tip of the tail, B–C, in order to be sure to get all the tail bone out. The front and hind legs are cut open on the underside, D–E, all the way to the hoof. In all antlered animals, the skin is cut open on top—never on the throat—and the ears skinned out (see Chapter 8). Remove the entire skin in one piece.

If the natural skull cannot be used, the head is carved from balsa wood (Figure 40). Pay close attention to details of the lips, nostrils, and eye sockets when carving the wood. If the natural skull is to be used, model on the face anatomy with modeling composition. The skull can be fastened to a supporting iron rod by anchoring the rod in the brain cavity with plaster of Paris.

Referring to the measurements taken when the animal was skinned, make a framework from iron rods. Shape these rods into position, copying the bends of the natural leg bones. (See Figure 41.) The rods are threaded to hold at the proper angle.

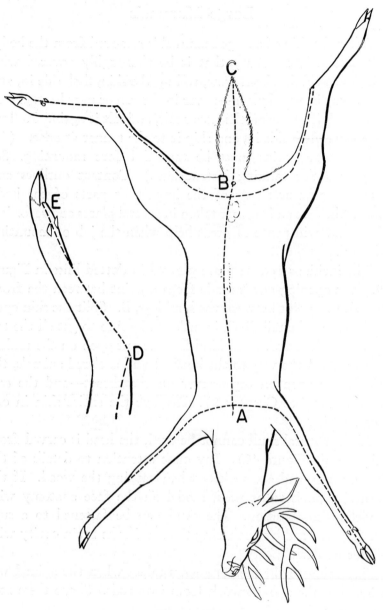

FIGURE 39

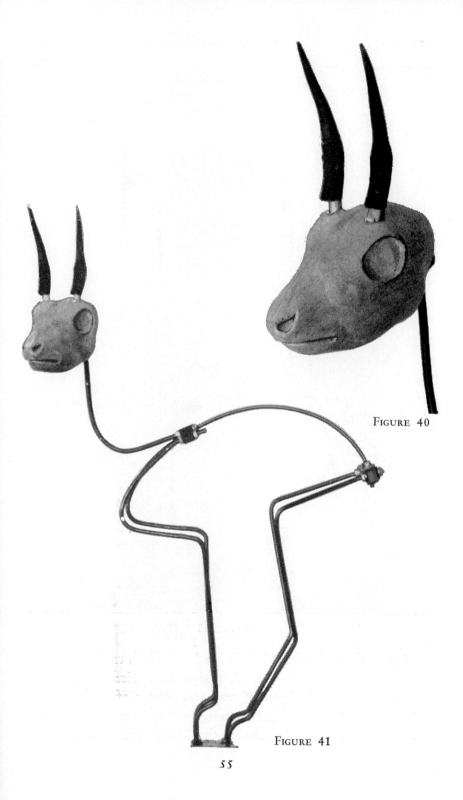

FIGURE 40

FIGURE 41

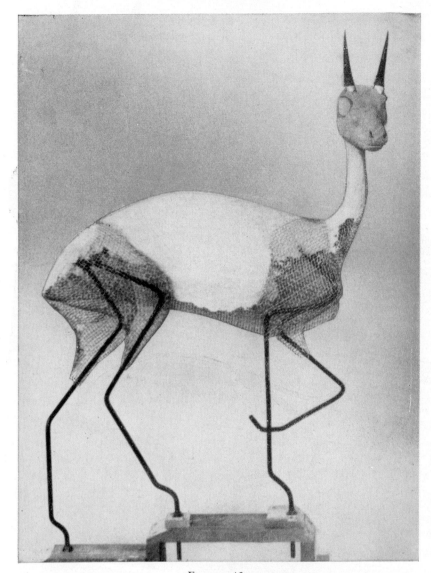

FIGURE 42

Cover the rods with ¼-inch hardware cloth to form the approximate size of the animal's body. This wire cloth is then covered with a thin layer of tow and plaster of Paris (Figure 42). When this has dried thoroughly, brush on shellac. This forms the core on which the artificial body is modeled.

FIGURE 43

Model the muscles and anatomy over this wire core with modeling composition, Formula #105, or papier-mâché. Ear cartilage is duplicated with a sheath of perforated lead, cut to proper size and fastened to the modeled head form (see Chapter 8). Glass eyes of correct size and color are set in place in the eye sockets. The model, when completed, should be an exact copy of the animal's natural body as it was after the skin was removed (Figure 43).

Insert the lead ear fillings in the ear skin, coating them first with body paste to hold them in place. Modeling composition can be worked around the base of the ears, eyes, lips, nostrils, and feet to fill out these parts so the skin will fit. The form is covered with thin body paste to allow the skin to be pulled over it and worked into position. Carefully sew all incisions together and, as the mount is drying, comb and brush the hair and check over the face and other details to improve the modeling. After the mount is dry, use oil paints to color all of the fleshy parts. If the animal has horns or antlers, these should be cleaned with a cloth moistened with turpentine and then oiled, Formula #108. This will give to the horns a natural luster. Figure 44 shows a well-mounted habitat group; African antelope, the Klipspringer.

Another method of mounting large mammals, now used in nearly all modern museums, is the Akeley method, named after Carl E. Akeley who developed it many years ago. Iron rods support both skull and leg bones and are anchored to a centerboard which supports the clay used to model the anatomy (Figure 45). The measurements and other data taken in the field are followed in setting up the skeleton. This framework is called the "armature."

Over this armature, modeling clay is applied to restore the details of the animal's anatomy (Figure 46). Again, the previous measurements are carefully followed until the model takes on the correct size and form of the animal's body as it was after the skin was removed.

FIGURE 44

59

FIGURE 45

FIGURE 46

FIGURE 47

Over the clay model, a layer of plaster of Paris and coarse fiber is applied, one section at a time, to make a mold. (Making the mold in several sections enables one to remove these sections intact from the model after the plaster hardens.) Notice, in Figure 47, the clay dam or partition over the neck and face

FIGURE 48

and around the body of the model. This sections off the plaster mold.

After the plaster hardens, the sections of the mold are re, moved from the clay model (Figure 48).

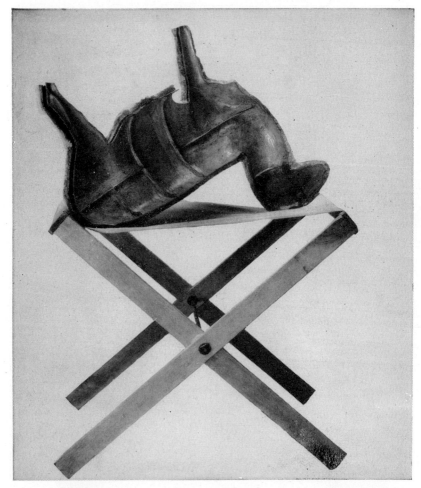

FIGURE 49

The "manikin" on which the skin will be drawn is next constructed by gluing into each section of the plaster mold several
layers of burlap supported with wood strips (Figure 49). The
sections of the mold are then fastened together until the burlap
dries. The plaster mold is then broken away leaving an exact
copy of the clay model in a hollow burlap form (Figure 50).
This form, or manikin, is very light in weight but strong enough
to receive and hold the tanned skin. The skin is poisoned and
worked over the manikin, after the latter has first been covered

FIGURE 50

with body paste to allow the skin to be adjusted and cemented into position.

All incisions are now sewed together, glass eyes of correct size and color set in place, and details of the face modeled. The hair is brushed and combed and the animal allowed to dry. The

FIGURE 51

specimen illustrated in Figure 51 is an African antelope, Soemmerring's Gazelle. Figure 52 shows a habitat group of white-tailed deer, reproduced in a winter setting. These were among the first to be mounted by Carl Akeley using the now famous method which bears his name.

FIGURE 52

67

Chapter 7

FISH AND REPTILES

In the mounting of fish and reptiles, the painting, or coloring of the completed mount is most important. Many well-mounted specimens are ruined by a poor job of coloring due either to an ignorance of the colors to be used, or to the lack of skill in applying them. Again, one must profit by experience and careful experiment.

Care must be exercised at all times in the mounting of fish and reptiles, for the mount must look as lifelike as possible. Pose the specimen in a characteristic position with a natural curve to the body, and give much thought and care to the application of the colors; the mount should not look as though it had just been painted.

Mounting Fish

Color Notes

As soon as possible after the fish has been collected, make accurate color notes, including notations of the eye color. This is very important since the natural colors, especially in fish, begin to fade immediately. A contact outline should also be made by laying the specimen on a piece of paper in the position desired for the finished mount, and tracing around the body with a pencil. Measurements of thickness should be made at intervals along the body and tail and noted beside the part of the outline to which they correspond.

Preliminary Steps

Should it be necessary to keep the fish for some time before working on it, wrap in a damp towel or put it in a thick bed of moss and pack in cracked ice. Be sure to replace the ice as

FIGURE 53

it melts. Do not postpone skinning any longer than necessary, however, since both fish and reptiles spoil soon after they are dead.

Before skinning, wash the specimen in cold running water, making certain that the inside of the mouth and gills are thoroughly clean. After washing, sponge off the fish with alum water, Formula #109. This solution will help remove the mucus with which all fish are covered. Now select the more perfect of the two sides (called the "show" side), to determine in which direction the mounted fish will face. The fish is then ready for casting, skinning, and mounting.

Cut the fish open on the off side (not the "show" side), and remove the entrails, filling in the cavity with sand or fine corn meal. Then sew the incision together. This will fill out the fish and give it a roundness which will make a more accurate plaster mold. Remember to keep the fish damp during the skinning and mounting process with the carbolic-acid-water solution, Formula #104.

Skinning

Pose the fish in a box or pan of sand, as shown in Figure 53, placing a newspaper on top of the sand so the sand will not stick to the specimen. Cut off the pectoral fin, *A*. Spread the fins and tail, and hold them in position with pins or wires as shown. Be sure the specimen is in the position the mount should have when completed, as it will not be possible to change this position once the plaster mold has been made.

Add ½ teaspoonful of alum to a quart of water. Into this alum-water sift, very slowly, No. 1 molding plaster until it has the consistency of heavy cream. Allow this plaster mixture to stand a few minutes before using. *Do not* stir. Starting at the head, pour the plaster over the body as illustrated in Figure 54,

FIGURE 54

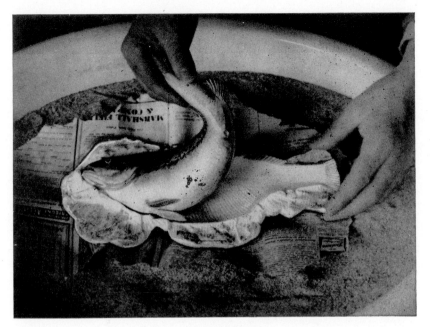

FIGURE 55

but do not cover the fins or tail. Make this plaster body mold thick and allow it to set until warm, then cold to the touch.

After the plaster has set, remove all pins or wires by twisting them slightly to work loose. Lift the mold with the fish in it, turn it over and, by grasping the tail, ease up the body from the mold to prevent curling of the scales (Figure 55). Be sure to remove the specimen as soon as the plaster has set thoroughly. The mold is now set aside to be used later in the mounting process.

Turn the fish on the opposite side from which the mold was made ("show" side down), and remove the skin. In skinning, start from in back of the head and cut down the middle, shown as line A–B in Figure 56, to the tail. This is the only cut made in skinning fish. Use a pair of scissors, a sharp knife, or a scalpel, cutting through the scales and skin, but no deeper. Be sure to keep the fins and tail moist.

FIGURE 56

FIGURE 57

72

Work the skin carefully down each side of the body being careful not to leave any more meat on the skin than is necessary (Figure 57). When the bases of the fins and tail are reached, a heavy pair of scissors must be used to cut through the bone and sever these parts from the body.

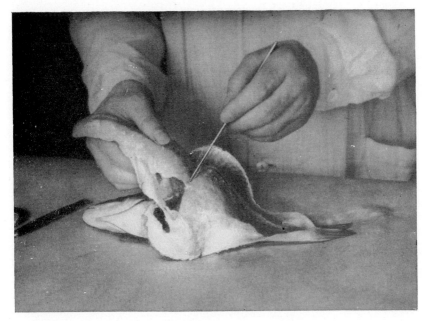

FIGURE 58

Continue skinning each side. Cut the tail from the body and work the skin off over the back until the head is reached (Figure 58). Again using the scissors, cut the body from the head close to the skull.

Clean the skin of all remaining pieces of flesh, always scraping from tail toward the head (Figure 59). Use a dull knife or a skin scraper for this so that no cuts will be put in the skin. Be careful in this cleaning operation not to injure the silvery lining next to the skin. Clean the head thoroughly, removing the eyes and cheek muscles. The latter can be taken out through the eye cavities. Do not remove the gills but cut away all flesh around them as well as any flesh or muscles around the fins and tail. After thoroughly scraping the skin, wash it in cold running water and allow it to drain.

Now dip the cleaned skin in a 70 per cent solution of grain or denatured alcohol and water. (Never use wood alcohol.) This bath helps to "set" the skin. Work the skin in this solution until it is saturated, then remove and drain. Brush on a weak

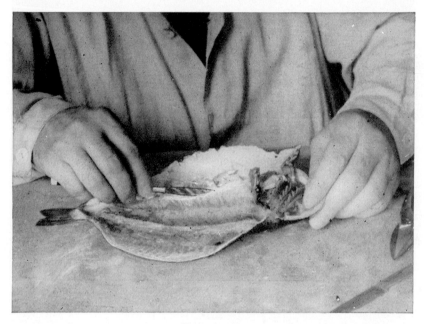

FIGURE 59

solution of formaldehyde around fins and tail and, with care, in the head cavity and around the gills. Brush the formaldehyde *only* on these parts. Now apply the preserving solution, Formula #103, to the rest of the inside of the skin.

Mounting

The treated skin is now laid out in the plaster mold and adjusted or pressed into the depressions (Figure 60). Hold the head and tail in their correct positions with pins or wires.

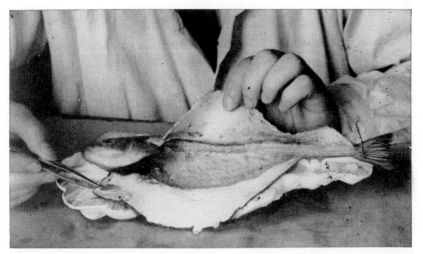

FIGURE 60

Mix a batch of papier-mâché and pour in a layer on the inside of the skin (Figure 61). Cut a small block of wood, *A,* and set it into place. Thicken the mâché and fill in the balance of the skin. Then, starting at the tail and working toward the head, sew the skin together.

FIGURE 61

FIGURE 62

The plaster mold acts as a guide and allows the specimen to be formed into a lifelike position (Figure 62). Be sure the fish is correctly posed before allowing the papier-mâché to set.

After the mâché has set, remove fish from mold (Figure 63). Fasten to a temporary panel of wood by screws through the back of the panel into the block of wood inside the specimen.

Spread the fins and tail, giving to them the curve and position of a live fish, and hold them in position with pieces of cardboard secured with pins or wires (Figure 64). Close the mouth. (If it is desired that the mouth be open, however, prop it open with small blocks of wood.) Pin down or spread open the gill coverts, as is desired. Fill in the cheek muscles (through the eyes) with papier-mâché. The pectoral fin, A in Figure 64, which has been kept moist, can also be spread and held open with cardboard and wires, then fastened into position with a small wire run into the body. Allow the specimen to dry thoroughly. This may take several weeks, depending upon the size of the fish and the climate.

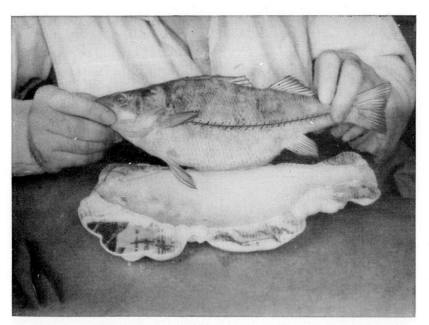

FIGURE 63

A

FIGURE 64

After the specimen is thoroughly dry, remove the cardboard and pins from the fins and tail, and any wires or blocks of wood that were used to keep parts in position. The fins and tail are now reinforced with cloth and tissue paper. Tear very fine cheesecloth into small pieces and glue them to the underside of the fins and tail (Figure 65). On the top side, glue a piece of tissue paper. Tear, do not cut, the cloth or paper, and use with the rough edges so that there will not be a straight edge showing on

FIGURE 65

the finished mount where the parts were reinforced. Use a special glue (Formula #110) for this work. After the glue has dried, trim the cloth and paper with a pair of sharp scissors, following the natural outline of the fins and tail.

Any depressions that occur in the specimen while it is drying can be filled in with composition or papier-mâché. Glass eyes of the correct color are now set in the eye sockets and held there with modeling wax. After all "pointing up" has been finished, give the fish a very thin coat of *new*, white shellac and allow it to dry. Referring again to the color notes, apply colors to make

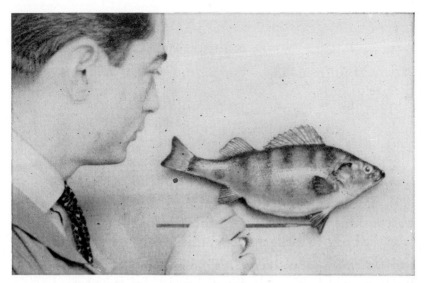

FIGURE 66

the mounted fish look lifelike (Figure 66). Use tube oil colors mixed with boiled linseed oil and turpentine. Be careful not to apply too much color, or the specimen will have a painted look that must be avoided. After colors have dried, give the mount a light coat of artist's picture varnish to restore some of the natural luster. Figure 67 shows a well-mounted perch.

FIGURE 67

Large Fish

In mounting very large fish, especially those of the salt-water variety, a different technique is required not only because of the size of these fish, but also because of the texture of the skin.

The "show" side of the fish is chosen and the pectoral, ventral and "sail" or dorsal fins are carefully cut away from the body. These are kept pliable in carbolic-acid-water solution.

The fish is laid out on a flat surface larger than the total length of the specimen, and given the shape and curve desired in the finished mount. The mucus is washed off with the alum-water solution, and a heavy mixture of plaster of Paris is poured over the body to make a strong, thick mold. The plaster mold should extend from just beyond the eye to behind the point where the tail joins the body. Allow the plaster to set, remove the fish from the mold, and proceed to remove the skin.

The opening cut is made on the "off" side (Figure 68, A), and the skin removed by the same method used with smaller fish. The skin is then scraped and cleaned of all particles of flesh. The eyes and gills are removed and all flesh and muscles around the head and at the base of the tail and fins cut away. The skin is next washed in cold running water, drained, and salted dry. The salt, which toughens the skin, must be rubbed all over the flesh side after the skin is thoroughly cleaned. Reinforce the plaster mold with 1-inch by 1-inch strips of wood, run lengthwise along the outside of the mold. Any bubbles on the inside of the mold must be filled in. The mold is then smoothed with sandpaper. Sections are cut out for the fins to rest in when the skin is replaced in the mold (Figure 68, B).

After allowing the skin and mold to dry for a day or two, all salt is washed off. The skin is then preserved by brushing on Formula #103. It is next placed in the mold and carefully adjusted into position so that all parts fit exactly where they belong. Soft water-clay (modeling clay made pliable with water) is then pushed tight against the inside of the skin to keep it in position (Figure 68, C). The clay is worked evenly over

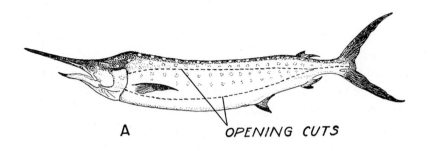

A   OPENING CUTS

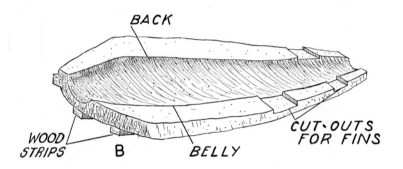

BACK

WOOD
STRIPS

B   BELLY

CUT·OUTS
FOR FINS

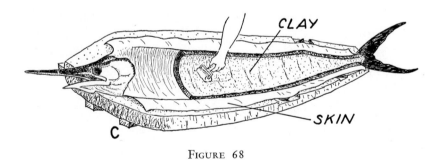

CLAY

C

SKIN

FIGURE 68

81

the skin, using the hands and a modeling tool so that the loose skin will conform to the plaster mold and take on the shape it had before the body was removed. Do not apply the layer of clay too thickly; about 1 inch is sufficient for a fish the size of the one illustrated.

Plaster of Paris is again mixed and poured in over the clay to form a core which will hold both the clay and the skin in position against the inside of the mold. The plaster is used only as a core and will be removed later; do not use any more than necessary.

After this has dried, place a board over the back and carefully turn the mold over; the board will serve as a support to the skin, clay, and plaster core, preventing them from falling out. The mold is now removed, and the tail and all fins that have been left attached to the skin are stretched and fastened into position on the board between heavy cardboards and secured with wires.

Allow the fish to dry for several days (the larger the fish, the more time required). After it is completely dry, carefully place the plaster mold back in its original position over the specimen, turn the mold over again, and remove the plaster core and then the clay. Allow the fish to dry several more days, watching to see if the skin pulls away from the inside of the mold. If it should pull away, dampen with carbolic-acid-water solution and hold only that part tightly against the mold with clay and plaster until dry.

After brushing out all dirt and clay dust, cover the inside of the skin with papier-mâché. Pour in several layers of the mâché, permitting each layer to dry before adding another. Shape a piece of hardwood to conform to the inside of the mold after the mâché has been added and set this in place securely with more mâché. The wood core will serve as a base to support the specimen later. Now sew the skin together and allow it to dry.

All fins which were removed from the specimen will have to be shaped separately and dried into position. The "sail," which is an important feature of the specimen illustrated, is spread into

position and glued to a piece of plywood ⅛-inch thick with carpenter's glue. (Add approximately 10 per cent glycerine to
the glue to keep it pliable and prevent cracking.) It is held securely with strips of heavy cardboard and pins while drying.
The "sail," when dry, is cut out of the plywood, along the
natural outline of the fin. The edges of the plywood are then
beveled. Mounting the fins on a wood base not only holds them
in position, but insures good support.

FIGURE 69

When the specimen has dried thoroughly, a cut the length of
the "sail" is made along the back of the mounted fish and the
"sail" set in. It is then held in place with wood screws that
have been worked through the plywood and into the hardwood core.

It will take several weeks for a large fish to dry thoroughly.
When it is completely dry, colored glass eyes are set in position
and all depressions around the face and at the base of the tail and
fins filled out with wax or mâché and sanded down until smooth.
The specimen is then colored with oil paints to reproduce the
color pattern it had in life. Figure 69 shows a well-mounted sail-
fish. The colors of the mount give it a lifelike appearance.

Snakes

Snakes can be mounted by much the same technique employed in the mounting of fish. Careful thought should be exercised in selecting the desired pose; too extreme a position will require a complicated mold and the beginner is apt to have difficulty in adjusting the skin during the mounting process. It

FIGURE 70

is important also to take accurate color notes as soon as the snake is collected.

Select the rock, log, or type of base wanted for the mount, and cover it with waxed paper. Pose the snake on top, fitting its coils carefully to the contours of the paper-covered base. Now make a plaster of Paris mold, following the same procedure described in the mounting of fish.

In skinning snakes, the incision is made down the belly from the center of the lower jaw to the tip of the tail. The body is removed, and the skin scraped, cleaned, and preserved as with fish. The skin is then fitted back into the plaster mold and filled out with papier-mâché.

Instead of the block of wood used when mounting fish, bend two or three wires in the shape of a large hairpin and set in at different places along the belly with the ends protruding through the skin where the incision is to be sewed together. These wires are used to anchor the snake to its base. Now begin at the tail and sew the incision together, using a very fine stitch.

After the specimen has been allowed to dry, restore the colors the snake possessed in life by referring to the color notes taken previously. Use care in painting on the colors to avoid giving the mount a painted look.

An excellent effect has been achieved in the mount shown in Figure 70 by the use of a piece of log as a base.

Frogs

There are several methods by which frogs can be mounted; two ways will be described below. The second method is somewhat more complicated but will reward painstaking efforts with excellent results.

First of all, color notes should be taken of the specimen. The frog should then be washed in cold running water and sponged off with the alum-water solution, Formula #109.

In order to skin a frog through the mouth, first force the mouth wide open and disjoint the neck where it joins the skull. Then gradually force the body through the mouth in much the same way as one removes a glove from the hand by turning it wrong side out.

When the legs are reached, each is skinned down to the foot as far as possible and cut off. This allows the body and legs to skin out through the mouth in one piece. Skinning a frog by this method, although somewhat confusing at first, does away with any sewing or waxing later.

Another method of skinning is to make a cut as shown by the dotted line *A–B* in Figure 71. The body is skinned out through this opening in much the same way as was described for fish. When the legs are reached, the leg bones are severed from the body at *C* and left attached to the skin. Only the body is removed through this opening. Now turn back the skin on each of the legs, working it well down over the leg muscles until the foot is reached. Leave all the leg bones attached, but cut away the flesh and muscles close to the foot.

Notice that, in skinning by the first method, there are no cuts in the skin. The skull is not disturbed, but left attached to the skin, but the body and all leg bones are removed. With the second method, one cut is made and the body removed from the skin, but all leg bones, after cutting away the flesh and muscles, are left attached at the feet.

The eyes are next removed. After this, small pieces of flesh adhering to the skin are cut away and the skin is made ready for mounting. Wash it well in cold running water to remove all blood and body fluids, then dip it in alcohol to "set" it. Immerse it in the preserving solution, Formula #103 (Borax), and work in this solution with the hands. Remove the skin and allow it to drain, but not to dry. Keep it wet at all times with the carbolic-acid-water solution while working. The skin must be kept damp and relaxed, or it will not "shape up."

If the frog has been skinned by the first method—through the mouth—the mounting technique is quite easy. Select five wires: four of them the proper size to support the frog, the other, strong enough to support the head. Sharpen each of the wires on one end. Cut a piece of cork or balsa wood to a rectangular shape and slip it down the frog's mouth. Hold the core from the outside at about the center of the body with the fingers. The leg wires (which have been run through the bottom of the foot and up inside the leg) can be anchored in this wooden block. Be sure that each of the leg wires is fastened securely to the core, and that the core is about at the center of the body.

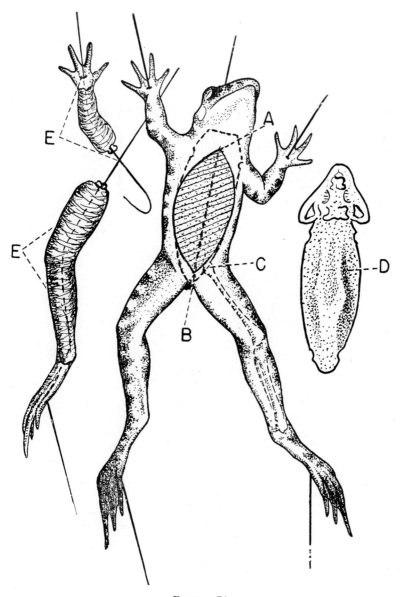

FIGURE 71

Work some of the modeling composition, Formula #105, down into each leg to where the bone was cut from the foot; this will help model that part of the leg in shape and will also serve to support the mount. Now secure some fine, hardwood sawdust and fill the specimen through the mouth, first down each hind leg and then gradually up the body around the wooden or cork core, into each of the front legs, and, finally, up the neck to the skull. A small stick, blunt end up (it can be cut out for

Chicago Natural History Museum

FIGURE 72

this purpose), will help pack the sawdust into place as the frog is filled and squeezed into shape. The wire that is to support the skull can now be shoved down through the head into the wooden core in the center of the body and anchored there.

Next, throat and eye cavities are filled and modeled with wax and the proper type of glass eyes adjusted into position. A few stitches taken in the lips will hold the mouth shut while the frog is manually shaped into the desired position. The wires in the legs and head will hold it in the correct shape until dry.

Another method, which is more complicated and requires quite a bit of skill and work, must be used if the frog is skinned by cutting it open. In Figure 71, the artificial body carved from balsa wood is shown at *D*. Note how it is shaped to fit into the skull. This carved body must have the exact size and shape of the body that was skinned out. It will be necessary to draw an outline of and measure the frog's body either before or after it is skinned.

Select four wires of the proper size for support and sharpen each at one end. Work each wire up along the leg bone, turning back the skin, and tie both together. They are next wrapped with very fine tow to replace the muscles that were cut away and covered with a coat of soft modeling composition. The legs may then be turned back into position. Figure 71 shows at *E* how the wires and leg bones are wrapped and shaped with tow, but care should be taken not to make the legs too large.

The carved wood body is now adjusted through the opening. The wires from each of the legs are run through this body and anchored firmly. Using composition, fill in any cavities where the legs are joined to the body and at the base of the skull; then sew up the incision.

The frog is now shaped into position. Glass eyes are set in place and the specimen permitted to dry thoroughly. It is advisable to punch a few holes all over the body with a needle so the skin will dry out slowly on the inside as well as the outside. After the specimen is dry, use modeling wax, Formula #107, to cover the incision and model on any depressions or shrinkage that might have occurred in the drying. The frog is then given one coat of white shellac. Working from the color notes taken earlier, apply all the proper colors and tints to make the mount look alive.

Figure 72 shows a mounted frog sitting on an artificial lily pad, the pad made from colored wax and cloth. Another frog, mounted by the second method described, is shown in Figure 73.

FIGURE 73

Turtles

The mounting of turtles is a fairly simple process since the shell constitutes most of the specimen and, being a hard substance, does not change to any great extent. The shell, however, also limits the number of positions that one can give the mount. For these reasons, a first attempt should prove quite satisfactory.

In skinning, only the bottom plate, called the "plastron," is removed. The legs, tail, and head remain attached to the upper shell, or carapace. The dotted line, A, in Figure 74, shows where the plate is attached to the shell; they are separated along this line by sawing. First, cut the skin loose around the lower edges of the plate, B, along the dotted line, until it can be removed and freed from the body. Before sawing where the plate and shell are joined, drill four holes on each side as shown. These holes will later be used in wiring the plate in place on the mounted turtle.

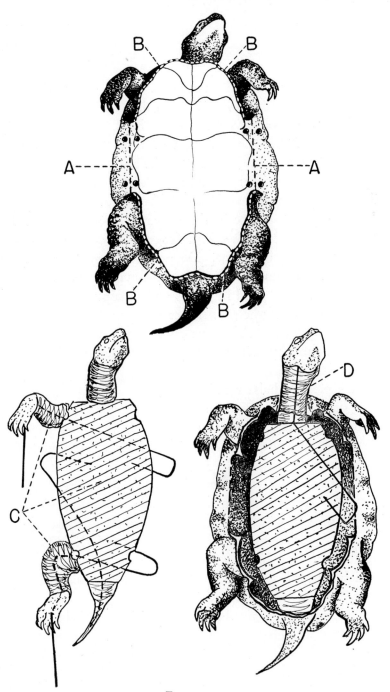

FIGURE 74

After removing this plate, skin out each of the legs and the tail by turning back the skin as you work. The muscles of the leg and the foot are cut away. Be sure to skin out the tail to the tip and remove the entire tail bone. The neck is skinned in a similar manner until the skull is reached. It is impossible, however, to work the skin over a turtle's head. The eyes, brain, tongue, and muscles of the face, therefore, must be removed from in back of the skull or through the mouth.

Next, wash the skin and bottom plate in cold running water until they are ·cleaned of all blood and body fluids. Then dip in alcohol and then immerse in the preserving solution, Formula #103. As with fish, snakes, and frogs, keep all the parts wet while in the mounting stage. Do not let them drain for too long a time after removal from the preserving solution or they will become dry and hard in places and difficult to work with.

Cut four wires of the proper size and length to support the mount and sharpen each at one end. These are for the legs. Now sharpen another wire for the tail, and one for the head and neck.

From a piece of balsa wood, shape a core that will fit snugly into the shell. Run a wire up through each of the legs, starting at the bottom of the foot and from the outside. Turn back the skin, rub the wire with wax to make it adhesive, and wind fine tow around it to replace the muscles cut away. Do the same for the tail and cover the tow with thin body paste, Formula #106. Now turn the skin of legs and tail back into position.

The manner in which legs, tail, and head are anchored to the balsa wood core is shown in Figure 74 at C and D. (The skin and shell, C, are not shown to simplify illustration.) Any cavities which exist where the legs, tail, or neck joins the body core can be filled out with composition.

The bottom plate is put back into position and held by small wires through the holes that were bored in the plate and shell. The edges of the skin are then sewed together. The throat and eye cavities are modeled with wax, and colored glass eyes of proper size set into place from the outside.

The turtle is now shaped into a characteristic position and is allowed to dry. After the mount is thoroughly dry, it is given a very light coat of white shellac. The proper colors can now be restored.

FIGURE 75

Figure 75 shows a mounted turtle with its mouth open. The tongue was modeled in the mouth with modeling wax, Formula #107. The inside of the mouth was then tinted with the proper color.

Chapter 8

GAME HEADS AND FUR RUGS

The mounting of animal heads, as trophies of the hunt and for display as game heads, and the making of fur rugs require somewhat similar techniques. Both will be treated in this chapter. Two methods are available for the mounting of game heads. The easier method is to purchase from a reliable taxidermy supply company a complete head form and simply pull the tanned or leathered scalp over this form. This method will save time and labor and produce good results. When ordering these forms, all measurements of the animal's head must be given in order to insure receiving a form that the scalp will fit.

As quickly as possible after the animal is collected, skin out the head, salt the skin, and get it to the tanner. Like all mammal skins that are to be mounted, head scalps must be tanned before a successful job can be accomplished (see Chapter 9). Do not delay the skinning or the scalp will spoil before it can be tanned.

Skinning

The opening incision of the skinning operation is always made on back of neck, never on the throat. Figure 76 shows the first cut as *A–B*. The cutting is continued from *A* to the base of each antler, and from *B* to *C* on both sides. Leave the neck skin long, with a part of the brisket attached. The scalp is removed from the head, working it first from around the base of each antler with a blunt tool. The ears are cut close to the skull and extreme care exercised when the eyes, nostrils, and lips are reached. Cut the lip linings close to the jaws and leave the cartilage of the nose attached to the scalp. Remove the head skin, or cape, in one piece.

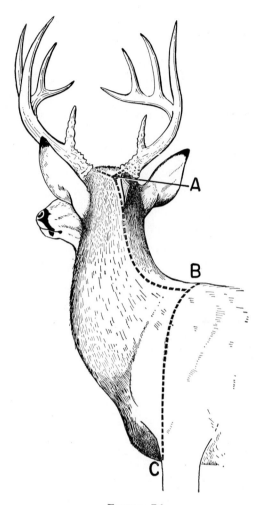

FIGURE 76

After the scalp is removed, cut away all pieces of meat and fat left clinging to it. Carefully turn and skin each ear inside out somewhat as a glove is removed from the hand. Clean all meat from the ear butts and work the ear skin loose from the back of the ear, shown in Figure 77 at A. Skin out to the tip and remove the cartilage, leaving only the ear lining shown in Figure 77 at B. The ears can be left turned inside out. Make a tracing of the ear cartilage to use as a guide when the artificial ears are cut out later. Nostrils and lips must be split open so that the salt with which the scalp is treated can penetrate all parts. Use a sharp knife in splitting open the nostrils and lips and work very carefully to avoid cutting through the skin. This part of the skinning operation of a game head will seem somewhat difficult at first, but by working slowly and examining the lips and nostrils as you proceed, you will see how they must be handled in the skinning.

After the head is skinned, ears turned, and lips and nostrils split open, salt is rubbed over all parts of the flesh side of the scalp. It is then rolled up, flesh side in. If the weather is damp, or if the scalp is a large one, it should be unrolled next day and the excess salt shaken off. It should then be resalted, rolled up and shipped to the tanner. If care is used in this salting process, the skin will be received by the tanner in good condition. He will then be able to return a well-tanned skin or scalp.

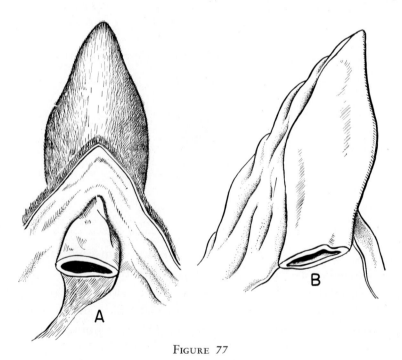

FIGURE 77

FIGURE 78

When mounting a head by the "head-form" method, only the antlers and the part of the skull which holds them together are saved. Notice, in Figure 78, that a cut is made through the skull at the top of the eye sockets, A. If you plan to use the "wrapped-skull" method (which will be explained later), do not cut off the antlers. (With this latter method, the entire skull is saved, cleaned of all flesh and put into boiling water to clean and remove all the meat.)

Mounting

The "head-form" method is by far the easiest and quickest way to mount a game head.   Notice, in Figure 79, that all details of the face and head anatomy are cast in the form.   At this time, a neck board will have to be cut and fitted to the back.

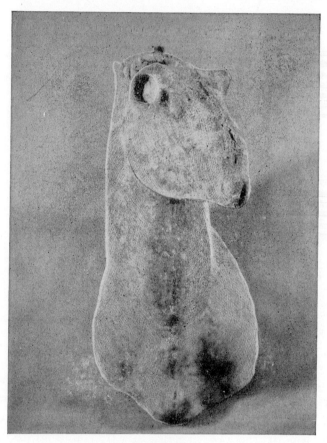

FIGURE 79

Trace the outline of the base of the neck on a 1-inch piece of clear board, saw out the area marked, and fit it into the neck opening of the form. Fasten by nailing through the form into the wood.

The antlers are set in position on the form and held there by two 3-inch wood screws run through the skull into a block of wood anchored in the form for this purpose. Model over the skull with papier-mâché to make it smooth as shown in Figure

FIGURE 80

80. (The nostrils and lips can be modeled on with papier-mâché, or with the modeling wax, Formula #107.) Properly colored glass eyes are set in the eye sockets and held there by the mâché or composition. Give attention to setting the eyes at the proper angle and depth, since the expression and lifelike

appearance of a mounted head depend upon how the eyes are set in. The ear cartilage which was removed is now duplicated with perforated lead. Using the tracing of the cartilage as a guide, cut the artificial ear linings from a sheet of perforated lead. These linings are now set in position on the form and the ear butts modeled in composition, Formula #105.

The tanned skin is now relaxed by brushing carbolic-acid-water solution, Formula #104, over the flesh side. The skin is then rolled up, flesh side in, and left overnight. If not relaxed enough the next day, this operation is repeated. After the skin is supple, it is poisoned by brushing the poisoning or preserving solution, Formula #103, on the flesh side. When the form has been covered with a thin layer of body paste, Formula #106, the scalp is ready to be pulled over the form and adjusted in place (Figure 81). If any cuts were put in the skin in the skinning or tanning operations, they must first be sewed together with a very small stitch that will not show.

In the first attempt at mounting a game head, one should work slowly, taking time with each step of the work. Try the tanned and relaxed scalp on the form before applying the body paste, to be sure it fits. Pull and stretch the skin, checking to see if it drapes properly and if the hair pattern falls into place. The body paste is first brushed over the face of the head form and the scalp then pulled and adjusted over that part, working to get the ears over the lead ear linings—the most difficult part. The skin can be held in place temporarily with twine or nails. Push and adjust the skin into position with the fingers and work out all air bubbles which will form under the skin at this time. Finish brushing on the body paste and pull the skin up and around the neck, holding it there, for the time being, with nails. Draw the skin well up under the antler burrs.

Using a furrier's curved needle and heavy waxed thread, sew together the incision on the back of the neck, starting at the base of the neck and working up to the point between the antlers, then following the cut to the base of each antler. Allow

FIGURE 81

enough of the neck skin to turn back over the baseboard and tack the skin to the board, placing the nails close together. Adjust the skin and fill in around the eyes, nostrils, and lips with modeling composition to give these parts the correct expression. The lips can be tucked into the composition and, if necessary, held in place with small brads. The black markings of the lips should be the same on each side of the face. The ears are set at the correct angle on the form and a small wad of excelsior inserted in the hollow of each ear to hold the skin in place. Wash away all body paste, or composition, before it dries by sponging warm water on the hair. After the hair is clean and while still damp, brush it well with a stiff hair brush.

A little extra attention while the head is drying will improve the modeling. Allow the head to dry thoroughly (this may take several weeks depending upon the climate), and then remove all wires and nails. Clean off any traces of composition from the eyes and lips and wax the eyes, the inside of the nostrils and ears, and the lips with modeling wax, Formula #107. This will build these parts up and render them more natural and lifelike. A small modeling tool is useful for this part of the work. Comb and brush the hair and oil the antlers with an oil solution, Formula #108. Rub this oil on with a soft cloth and wipe off any surplus. Where the skin was waxed or where colors have faded, oil colors are used to restore the natural tones which were present when the animal was collected.

When mounting a game head by the "wrapped-skull" method, the entire skull is saved and used as a base for the form. A baseboard to support the head is first cut from a 1-inch piece of clear wood. An iron rod of proper size and length is anchored into a plaster core in the brain cavity of the skull. The other end of the rod is fastened to the baseboard. The rod can then be bent into the position desired in the mount. Wire cloth is next placed around this rod to serve as a guide in shaping the head, and to hold the excelsior used to build up the neck and parts of the skull (Figure 82).

FIGURE 82

Coarse excelsior, slightly dampened, is tightly wrapped around the rod and wire cloth a little at a time, and held in place with twine (Figure 83). Excelsior is also used to fill in the eye sockets and where the nostrils and lips will be modeled. This excelsior form serves as a foundation on which to model the anatomy of face and neck and it must be wound tightly to give a firm base for modeling.

Using the modeling composition, Formula #105, all details of the head are put in place and all facial expression carefully modeled, following the data taken previously (Figure 84). One must have some experience in modeling and know the

FIGURE 83

anatomy of the animal's face to do this properly. Study of animals and practice in modeling are the only ways to acquire this skill. Anatomical charts, books on anatomy, and drawings of animals are all a great help in knowing the correct details to model.

When the modeled form is complete, allow the composition to dry thoroughly. Now shellac the entire head form to make it waterproof and provide a firm base on which to pull the tanned skin.

The tanned scalp is now relaxed and poisoned in the same way as that described in the "head-form" method. The form is

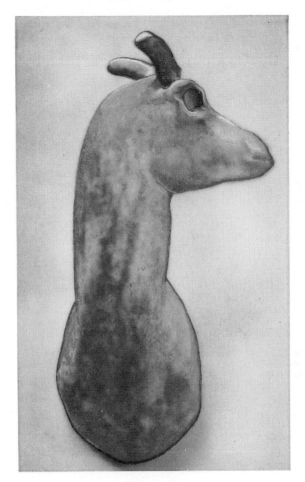

FIGURE 84

covered with body paste and artificial lead ear linings are inserted in the ear pockets. The head skin is pulled and adjusted into place over the form. The incision on the back of the neck is sewed together, the ears held in place with wires, and when dry the mounted head is finished in the same manner as was described in the discussion of the "head-form" method (Figure 85).

While some of these instructions may seem too brief, it must be remembered that as you proceed with the work you will more readily understand what is meant.

FIGURE 85

Fur Rugs

Animal skins which are to be made up as fur rugs must also be tanned (see Chapter 9). Rug heads should be mounted with the mouth open to achieve a more dramatic effect. As in the mounting of game heads, it is best to purchase the complete head form from a taxidermy supply company. Should one choose to do so, however, the natural skull can be saved and prepared by the same "wrapped-form" method used in mounting a game head. Figure 86 shows a head form, or shell—without teeth or tongue—for a rug head. These forms are made from a very light, but strong material. The head form, complete with artificial teeth and tongue, is illustrated in Figure 87.

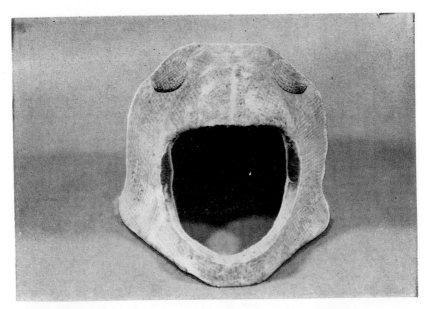

FIGURE 86

FIGURE 87

107

The natural teeth of the animal can be used, but in time they will crack and chip; artificial teeth are used in this illustration. Ready-made forms come complete with the inside of the mouth, lips, and tongue, all waxed and painted in lifelike colors.

The tanned head skin is made pliable with the carbolic-acid-water solution, Formula #104. When pliable, it is poisoned

FIGURE 88

by brushing on the preserving solution, Formula #103. (Poison only the head skin at this time.) Artificial ears can be cut from leather of the proper thickness, using the natural ears (cartilage) that were removed as a guide. These leather ear linings are now inserted in the ear pockets. The head form is covered with the body paste, Formula #106, and the skin pulled and adjusted over the form into position. Modeling composition, Formula #105, can be worked under the skin around the eyes, nostrils, and lips to help model and hold the skin in place on the form. Small brads or pins can also be used to accomplish this. Properly colored glass eyes are set into the eye sockets at the correct angle and depth and the eyelids adjusted to give a natural expression to the face (Figure 88). Comb and brush the hair and allow it to dry. All this work is done before making up the balance of the skin into a rug.

The body skin of the animal must be relaxed, stretched, and trimmed. Relax it by brushing the carbolic-acid-water solution, Formula #104, over the flesh side. Roll up, flesh side in, and allow to remain eight to twelve hours. Unroll it and repeat the application of the solution until the skin is pliable enough to work. Now stretch the skin on a table larger than the skin, or on the floor, making it even all around. In order to do this, it will be necessary to make some V-shaped cuts in the skin where wrinkles occur, illustrated at *A* in Figure 89. Cut away these V-shaped pieces of skin and sew the edges together. If this is properly done, the wrinkles will disappear and the skin will lie flat. If necessary, make a V-shaped cut at the base of the head, shown at *B* in Figure 89, so the head will lie in a straight line.

Now pull and stretch the skin, and nail it around the edges, placing the nails close together so that the entire body skin is stretched out evenly and without wrinkles. Allow to dry in this position. *Do not remove the nails until the skin is dry.*

After the skin is thoroughly dry, turn it over and poison it well on the flesh side. There are several ways in which to finish a fur rug. A good grade of cotton padding should be placed underneath the body skin to fill out the skin and prevent wear. Trim this padding to the outline of the rug and sew it securely to the body skin. Place an extra layer of padding under each foot. When the claws of the animal are very long, use three layers. It is not necessary to sew the padding completely around the edges. Sew it on only in enough places so that the skin will not come loose. Canvas or some similar material is used for the under lining. If a felt border is used (for a natural appearance, however, it is best not to use one), select a color for both the lining and the border which will harmonize with the color of the rug. The lining and border are sewed to the body skin at the same time with a strong, waxed thread and a furrier's curved

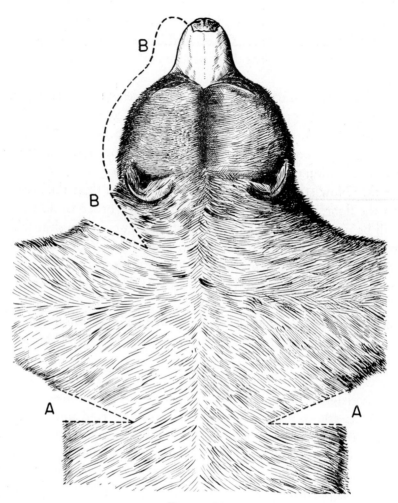

FIGURE 89

needle.   Make the stitches close together so that the skin will not gap open.   Figure 90 shows the body skin, *A*, the lining, *B*, and the felt border, *C*.

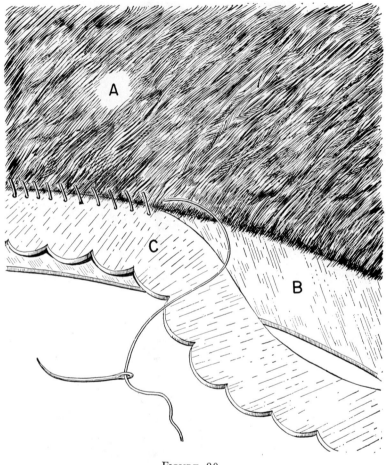

FIGURE 90

The rug is now combed and brushed until the hair falls into place and all dust is removed.   Oil colors are used to restore coloring to the skin around the eyes, nostrils, and lips.   Fur rugs that are subject to much wear must be combed and brushed often, and frequently aired, to keep them in excellent condition. Figure 91 shows two good examples of this branch of taxidermy.

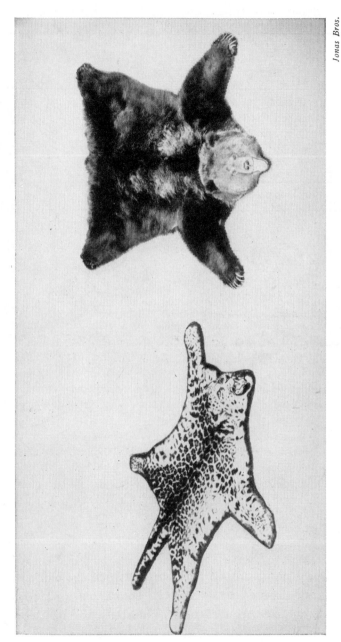

FIGURE 91

112

The heavier beam, shown in Figure 100, is constructed from a plank of hardwood 5 feet in length, 10 inches in width, and 1½ inches in thickness. The upper edges are rounded off over the full length. The height of this beam can be varied to suit the individual worker. The way in which heavier skins are worked over this beam is shown in Figure 101.

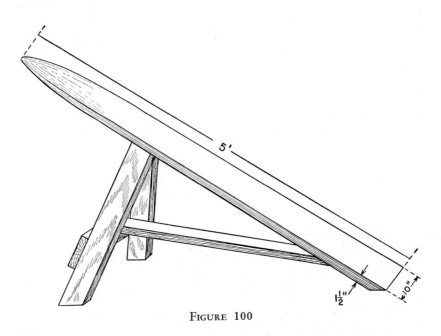

FIGURE 100

Preparing the Skins

All skins must be shaved and degreased before the tanning solutions can take effect. Before the skins are shaved or fleshed, however, certain preliminary steps must be followed. As soon as the skin is removed from the animal's body, the nostrils, lips, and area around the eyes are split open, and the ears turned inside out by splitting them open between the cartilage and skin (Figure 77). This step is very important since the solutions will not act on any part of the skin if the flesh is left on. The skin is now salted with common salt until the entire flesh side of

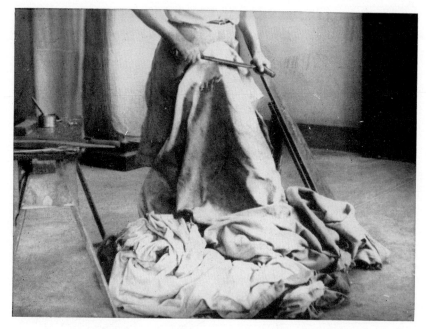

FIGURE 101

the skin is thoroughly covered. It is then rolled up, flesh side in, and left undisturbed for several days.

Skins which have been received in a dry, hard condition can be soaked in water containing a small amount of carbolic acid, Formula #104, until pliable. This will also keep them free of bacteria which cause the hair to slip. Should a skin become too soft and limp in this solution, add a little salt.

After the skin has been salted and laid away, it will be found to have dried out and become wrinkled. To restore it to the proper condition for shaving, it must be soaked overnight in a fairly strong solution of salt water containing a small amount of carbolic acid, and allowed to drain.

It is very important that all skins be shaved or fleshed until they are as thin as possible. No skin can be tanned so that it will stretch properly unless it is shaved thoroughly before the application of the tanning solutions. Experience is the important requirement at this stage of the tanning operation.

Degreasing

When all muscle and tissue have been shaved off and the skins are of the desired thickness any remaining fat must be degreased. To do this, soak smaller skins in naphtha solution thoroughly. Large skins are stretched out on the floor, naphtha sprinkled on both flesh and hair sides, and coarse hardwood sawdust rubbed in and worked well into the hair to absorb the naphtha and grease. Now shake or beat out all sawdust and wash the skin thoroughly in several rinses of clear water to remove any traces of salt remaining in the skins. Next, drain, but do not dry, the skin, and proceed with the tanning process.

Tanning

After the skins are thoroughly shaved or fleshed, degreased, and washed clean of all salt, they are stretched out on the floor, flesh side up, and wet down with a coating of the pickling solution, Formula #111. Next, sprinkle a small amount of sawdust over the flesh and repeat the application of the pickle, making certain that all parts of the skin are well covered. The sawdust will absorb some of the solution and keep it from running off the skin. Leave the skins stretched out on the floor overnight to allow the solution to penetrate through the flesh side, but do not let the skin dry out. Finally, the flesh side is covered with a coat of sulphonated neat's-foot-oil solution, Formula #112.

Now hang the skin up until it is thoroughly dry. Then dampen it with a solution of carbolic-acid-water. Roll it up, flesh side in, and lay it away overnight. The next day, the skin will be ready to be worked with the hands over the large beam. This work consists of stretching the skin in every way until it is soft and pliable. Again, hard work is called for. The skins must be worked until they have plenty of "life" and stretch.

Cleaning the Fur

After the skin has been thoroughly worked, lay it hair side up on the floor and sprinkle on a small amount of naphtha. Be

careful that the naphtha does not get on the flesh side, for it
will remove the oil. Now rub in sawdust to dry and cleanse
the hair. After the sawdust has been worked into the hair or
fur and has absorbed the naphtha, beat it out with a small, flex-
ible stick. This will also serve to "fluff" up the hair. (Heavier
hides must be dampened once again after this with the carbolic-
acid-water solution, rolled up, and put away overnight. The
next day these hides are pliable and in proper condition for a
final shaving over the fleshing beam.) Use extreme care at this
stage against putting any cuts in the skin. Lay the skin on the
floor once more and sponge on a mild solution of warm, soapy
water. Then roll it up, flesh side in, and lay it away overnight.
The next day it may be necessary to give the skin another light
coat of the sulphonated oil. The tanning process is now complete. The skin should be soft and pliable enough for mounting
or for being made into a rug.

Tanning with Alum

Tanning with alum is an easier method to leather skins. Although an old method, it is still used today by many professional
tanners.

Small skins that have been dried without preservatives and
those that have been salted must be relaxed by covering the flesh
side with sawdust dampened with carbolic-acid-water solution.
(Large or thick skins must be immersed in the solution to accomplish this.) After they are pliable, shave, degrease, and
clean them as previously described. Then immerse in the alum
solution, Formula #113.

After leaving the skins in this solution for about a week, remove them and allow them to drain. After draining, apply a
coat of the sulphonated-oil-water solution and allow the skin
to dry thoroughly. Then relax the skins once more with carbolic-acid-water solution and work them over the beam to make
them pliable. If a particularly fine job of tanning is desired,
the skins can again be shaved, oiled, and allowed to dry. When
dry, dampen once more and, again, gradually work them over

the beam until pliable. When they are cleaned with sawdust, the job is finished. If the skins have been well handled through-out the tanning process they will be, at this time, white all over the flesh side and very supple.

Tanning Without the Hair

To tan a skin and, at the same time, remove the hair or fur, the skin must be first soaked and fleshed and then placed in the solution, Formula #114. This will remove all the hair and leave the skin well cleaned on both sides. (Be sure that the skin is free of all dirt, salt, and fat, before placing it in this solution.) Be careful to soak the skin until the hair is loose and can be slipped or scraped off easily. The skin can be laid over the flesh-ing beam and the hair pushed off with the currier's knife. If the hair does not come off easily, put the skin back into the solu-tion once more. Remove, drain, and wash it out in warm water to remove the lime. Then neutralize any remaining lime by soaking the skin overnight in the solution, Formula #115. Work the skin occasionally with the hands in the solution. Re-move the skin and wash it thoroughly in several changes of clear water. Proceed with the tanning of the skin as described, but add 15 grams of chrome alum (dissolved) to the tanning liquid.

Tanning Snake Skins

The tanning of snake skins can be the most disappointing of all tanning jobs. This is due to several difficulties which vary with the type of skin being worked. Many formulas have been tried and new ones are being worked out all the time, but few are entirely successful. The following method, however, can be used for a number of skins.

If the skin is not fresh from the specimen, soak it in water until soft. The skin then is fleshed and put in a solution of lime and water, Formula #116. Allow the skin to soak for two or three days, or until the scales are loose, but not any longer. Now scrape away all scales with a stiff brush. (Snake skins can-not be successfully tanned with the scales remaining on the skin.) Before proceeding any further, it is most important to remove all lime from the skin. Do this by soaking it in the solution, Formula #115. Work the skin through this solution several times. Now make a weak solution of alum and salt, Formula #117. Place the skin in this solution and allow it to remain for three to four days. Dissolve 5 grams of sodium carbonate in a glass of warm water and add this to the solution, drop by drop, taking about twenty minutes to add it all. Keep the skin in this solution for six days, stirring once or twice each day.

Now remove the skin from the liquid, drain it, and soak it overnight in a weak solution of sulphonated oil (1 part oil to 3 parts water). Squeeze the liquid out of the skin, stretch it, and tack it on a board so that it can dry thoroughly. When dry, take it off the board and gently work it over the fleshing beam until it is soft and pliable. When the skin is dry and pliable, it must be gone over with a warm iron in the same way as a suit is pressed. Finally, apply a thin coat of liquid celluloid to the pattern side of the skin to give to it a new and glossy look.

Conclusion

Successful results in taxidermy can only be achieved by many hours of hard work and many years of practical experience. In a book of this kind, all that can be done is to give the methods and techniques to follow in the mounting of birds, mammals, and fish. Even while these techniques are being mastered, many hours should be spent in the study of living birds and animals, either in the wild state, or in zoos.

It is only by a combination of knowing what to do and the results wanted that one can become an experienced taxidermist. The outcome of a well-mounted bird or animal depends entirely on, first, your knowledge of the animal as it was in life, and, second, your experience in mounting that animal to look alive.

INDEX